STAR TREK
OTHER REALITIES

Star Trek created by
GENE RODDENBERRY

Star Trek: Deep Space Nine® created by
RICK BERMAN & MICHAEL PILLER

Star Trek: New Frontier™ concept by
JOHN J. ORDOVER & PETER DAVID

Cover Art JOHN VAN FLEET	**Design** LARRY BERRY
Editor JEFF MARIOTTE	**Special thanks to** PAULA BLOCK

STAR TREK: OTHER REALITIES 2001.
Published by WildStorm Productions, an imprint of DC Comics, under exclusive license from Paramount Pictures Corporation.
Editorial Offices: 7910 Ivanhoe St., #438, La Jolla, CA 92037. Cover, afterword, and compilation copyright © 2001 Paramount
Pictures. Originally published as STAR TREK: ALL OF ME, STAR TREK: DEEP SPACE NINE – N-VECTOR 1-4, STAR
TREK: NEW FRONTIER – DOUBLE TIME. Copyright © 2000 Paramount Pictures. All Rights Reserved. STAR TREK and
all related marks are trademarks of Paramount Pictures. DC Comics authorized user. Any similarities to persons living or dead are
purely coincidental. Printed in Canada. First Printing. DC Comics. A division of Warner Bros. – An AOL Time Warner Company

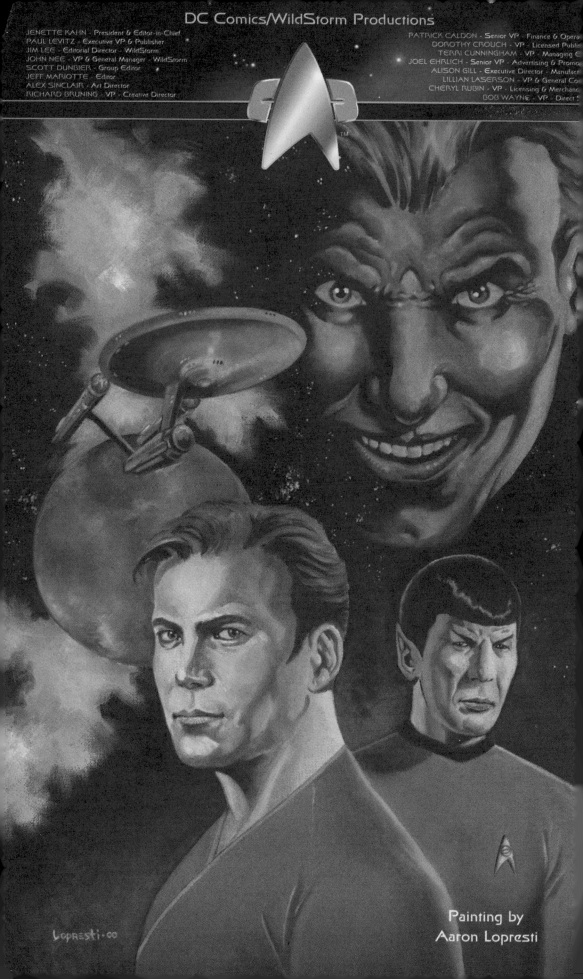

Painting by
Aaron Lopresti

Lopresti 00

CONTENTS

MAYBE I SHOULD SEW YOU UP WITH NEEDLES AND *CAT-GUT*, JIM. LEAVE A NICE *SCAR* TO GO WITH YOUR "CAPTAIN BLOOD" ATTITUDE.

WELL, YOU'LL LIVE FOR NOW. BUT WOULD YOU MIND TELLING ME *WHY* YOU DID THIS?

ORION'S BEEN CLAIMING NEUTRALITY FOR YEARS, BONES, WHILE ITS *PIRATE* SHIPS RAID THE OUTER COLONIES.

WHEN THEIR SHIPS FACE CAPTURE, THEY SELF-DESTRUCT... AND ORION DISAVOWS THEM AS "*ROGUES.*"

WE NEEDED TO CAPTURE ONE *INTACT*.

WE BEAMED ONTO THEIR SHIP WHEREVER OUR SENSORS DETECTED LIFE FORMS...TO CATCH THEM *BEFORE* THEY COULD BLOW THEMSELVES UP.

WE COULDN'T EVEN RISK USING OUR *UNNN* PHASERS FOR FEAR OF DAMAGING THE SHIP.

Fwoosh

THAT LEG WILL BE TENDER FOR A WHILE. THINK I'LL GO BACK TO THE BRIDGE WITH YOU SO I CAN ENJOY WATCHING YOU WINCE.

I THOUGHT YOU'D *APPRECIATE* THE STRATEGY, BONES.

IT'S CALLED A *SURGICAL* STRIKE.

GOOD ANSWER, WRONG QUESTION. WHY *YOU*, JIM? YOU HAVE AN OUTSTANDING CREW...

WHY DO YOU ALWAYS PUT *YOUR* LIFE ON THE LINE?

COMMAND PSYCHOLOGY. YOU NEVER ASK-- *I* NEVER ASK MY CREW TO DO SOMETHING I'M NOT PREPARED TO DO *MYSELF*.

CAPTAIN KIRK... WE HAVE A MESSAGE COMING IN FOR YOU FROM *STAR FLEET*.

PUT IT ON THE MAIN SCREEN, LT. UHURA. I'M ON MY WAY.

"HIS PARENTS WERE SUCCESSFUL, AFFLUENT, AND *ARDENT* PARTICIPANTS IN EARTH'S *SOCIAL* ACTIVITIES.

"THEY WERE, HOWEVER, WOEFULLY *ILL-EQUIPPED* TO BE PARENTS, FAR MORE INVOLVED WITH THEIR *OWN* CONCERNS THAN WITH THE RAISING OF THEIR *SON.*

"HE GREW UP WITH A SUCCESSION OF *NANNIES,* ALL OF WHOM HE RESENTED. HIS PARENTS DENIED HIM *NO* MATERIAL THING...BUT IT WAS ONLY THROUGH ILL-TEMPERED DISPLAYS AND TANTRUMS THAT HE WAS ABLE TO GAIN THEIR *ATTENTION.*

"ON REACHING THE AGE OF CONSENT, AND MUCH TO THE *DISPLEASURE* OF HIS PARENTS--

"--ST. JOHN ENTERED *STARFLEET ACADEMY.*

"PERHAPS BECAUSE *MY* ATTENDING THE ACADEMY CAUSED A RIFT WITH MY FATHER, ST. JOHN CONSIDERED ME HIS *ONLY* FRIEND -- THE ONLY PERSON CAPABLE OF UNDERSTANDING HIS *GENIUS.*

"NEVERTHELESS, I CONSIDERED THE SHORTCUTS HE EMPLOYED IN HIS RESEARCH *IRRESPONSIBLE.*

"WE QUARRELED FREQUENTLY.

"HE WAS *EXPELLED* FROM THE ACADEMY AFTER ONE OF HIS EXPERIMENTS CAUSED EXTENSIVE DAMAGE TO THE CAMPUS.

"AN *UNFORTUNATE* END TO HIS STARFLEET CAREER."

"CAPTAIN'S LOG, STARDATE 6619.4: THE ENTERPRISE HAS ESTABLISHED STANDARD ORBIT AROUND POLLUX II..."

"...TO DISCOVER THAT ARMAND ST. JOHN IS EVERY BIT AS *DIFFICULT* AS SPOCK ADVISED."

IT'S ABOUT *TIME* YOU ARRIVED, *ENTERPRISE.* DIDN'T STARFLEET APPRAISE YOU OF THE *IMPORTANCE* OF MY DISCOVERIES HERE?

OUR *APOLOGIES,* MR. ST. JOHN. WE WERE A CONSIDERABLE DISTANCE WHEN WE *RECEIVED* YOUR REQUEST.

PERHAPS IF THIS VESSEL HAD *TRANSWARP* DRIVE, WE COULD'VE MADE BETTER TIME.

DON'T ATTEMPT BANTER WITH ME, CAPTAIN. TO USE MILITARY PARLANCE, YOU ARE CONSIDERABLY *OUTGUNNED.*

WHERE'S *SPOCK?* HE'S THE ONLY ONE ON YOUR SHIP WITH WHOM I REALLY WISH TO CONVERSE.

I AM HERE, ARMAND.

FEEL FREE TO LET YOUR *CAPTAIN* TAG ALONG AS WELL, OLD FRIEND.

EXCELLENT! I CANNOT *WAIT* FOR YOU TO WITNESS MY LATEST DISCOVERY.

JUST DON'T ASK ME TO STOP AND *EXPLAIN* EVERYTHING TO HIM.

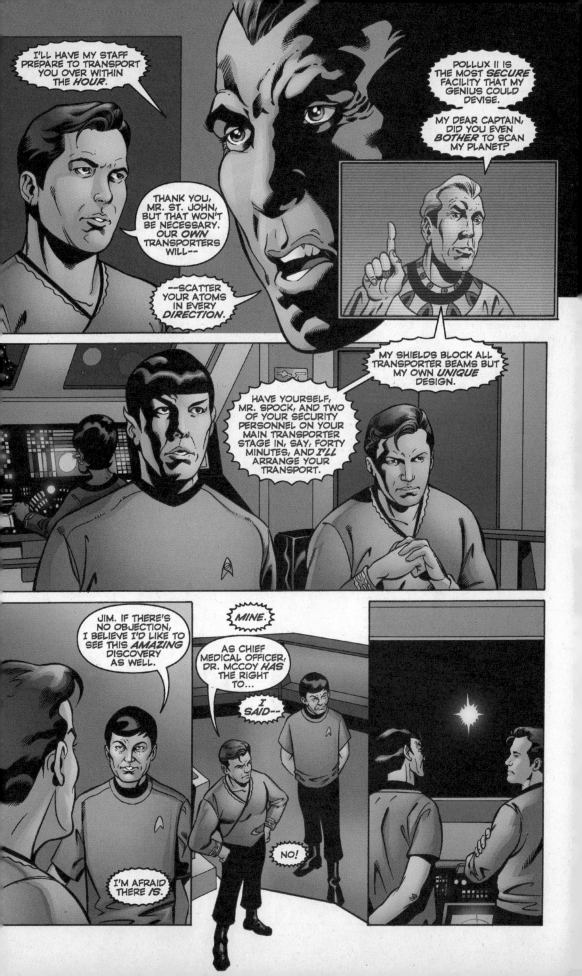

WHAT IN THE SEVEN GALAXIES...

WHAT'S THE *MEANING* OF THIS?

I AM CERTAIN THAT IS A QUESTION MR. ST. JOHN WOULD PREFER TO ANSWER HIMSELF. THIS WAY, GENTLEMEN.

SPOCK, EXPLANATION?

I HAVE NONE, CAPTAIN. I AM AS AT A LOSS TO UNDERSTAND THIS AS YOU.

COULD THEY BE CLONES?

DOUBTFUL. I HAVE OBSERVED REPRESENTATIVES OF AT LEAST ONE HUNDRED FORTY-SEVEN DIFFERENT RACES HERE, EACH OF THEM RESEMBLING ARMAND ST. JOHN.

THE TECHNOLOGY TO COMBINE GENETIC MATERIAL IN THIS MANNER IS QUITE BEYOND OUR PRESENT CAPABILITIES.

EVEN FOR ARMAND ST. JOHN.

GENTLEMEN, ARMAND ST. JOHN AWAITS YOU. HE WILL ANSWER ALL YOUR QUESTIONS.

DO COME IN.

SPOCK!

AND CAPTAIN. AS MY OTHER SAID, DO COME IN. NO NEED TO STAND ON CEREMONY.

I DON'T BLAME YOU FOR GAZING SO LONGINGLY AT THAT PARTICULAR OTHER, CAPTAIN.

LOVELY, AREN'T I?

MR. ST. JOHN, WHAT--EXACTLY--IS GOING ON HERE?

YOU MEAN SPOCK HASN'T DEDUCED THAT AS YET?

HOW DISILLUSIONING!

I HAVE A THEORY. HOWEVER, WITHOUT ADDITIONAL DATA, I AM RETICENT TO VOICE IT.

HA HA! WONDERFUL! THE SAME OLD SPOCK!

AS TACITURN AND CAREFUL AS EVER!

AM I TO UNDERSTAND THAT YOU BELIEVE YOU UTILIZE THIS *CONSIDERABLE* AMALGAMATION OF MACHINERY--

--TO SEEK OUT AND COLLECT ALTERNATE REALITY VERSIONS OF *YOURSELF?*

BELIEVE, SPOCK? IT'S MORE THAN SIMPLE *BELIEF.*

LOOK AROUND YOU, MAN. I'M *DOING* IT!

AND *VIOLATING* THE PRIME DIRECTIVE.

OR DIDN'T IT *OCCUR* TO YOU HOW COLLECTING THESE OTHERS WOULD AFFECT THE WORLDS YOU TOOK THEM FROM?

THERE'S NO TELLING *WHAT* YOUR ALTERNATES MAY HAVE BEEN DOING-- HOW ESSENTIAL THEY ARE TO THEIR OWN UNIVERSES.

AND YOUR MACHINE *DEPRIVES* THOSE UNIVERSES OF THEM.

HOW *DARE* YOU? YOU INSIGNIFICANT--

I WOULD NOT WORRY *OVERMUCH* ABOUT POSSIBLE EFFECTS ON ANY ALTERNATE UNIVERSES, CAPTAIN.

MR. ST. JOHN IS CLEARLY *NOT* COLLECTING HIS DUPLICATES FROM THEM.

MR. SULU, THERE ARE REPORTS OF *PHASER* FIRE COMING IN FROM ALL OVER THE *ENTERPRISE!*

WHAT?!

"ENEMY PARTIES ARE BEAMING INTO THE SHIP!"

"WE'RE BEING BOARDED!"

NCC-1701-7

MR. SULU!

ALL SHIELDS UP--FULL POWER!

SECURE THE BRIG!

A BIT *LATE* FOR THAT, MY FRIEND. WE'VE ALREADY FREED YOUR GUESTS AND *TAKEN* YOUR SHIP. WHAT *YOU* MUST DECIDE IS DO YOU WISH TO SURRENDER POSTHASTE--

--OR *POSTHUMOUSLY?*

"CAPTAIN'S LOG, STARDATE 6619.7: ARMAND ST. JOHN'S PLANS FOR THE *ENTERPRISE*-- WHATEVER THEY MAY BE--SEEM TO HAVE HIT A SNAG. *SCOTTY'S* DOING, NO DOUBT."

MY KLINGON SELF RECOMMENDS *TORTURE* TO ACQUIRE YOUR MR. SCOTT'S NEW PROGRAMMING LANGUAGE. HE HASN'T QUITE GRASPED THAT OUR RULE IS TO BE A *BENIGN* ONE.

ADMIRAL ST. JOHN, ON THE OTHER HAND, SUGGESTED ONE OF OUR SPOCKS USE THE VULCAN *MIND MELD.*

THAT'S THE *MILITARY* FOR YOU. NEVER HAD MUCH FAITH IN THAT VULCAN MUMBO-JUMBO *MYSELF.* BESIDES--

--HOW DIFFICULT COULD IT BE FOR A PERSON OF OUR-- *OUR* INTELLECT TO DECIPHER MR. SCOTT'S SIMPLE CODES?

EXACTLY WHAT DID YOU MEAN BY *"OUR RULE?"*

EXACTLY *WHICH* WORD WERE YOU HAVING THIS DIFFICULTY *UNDERSTANDING*, CAPTAIN?

"OUR" OR *"RULE?"*

SIMPLY PUT, THE *FEDERATION* IS A SHAMBLES. QUARRELSOME FACTIONS *WITHIN* YOUR COTERIE THREATEN TO TEAR YOUR FRAGILE ALLIANCE ASUNDER--

--WHILE ENEMIES FROM *WITHOUT* ACCELERATE THAT INEVITABLE COLLAPSE.

I HAVE LONG KNOWN THAT ONLY SOMEONE OF *MY* INTELLECT WAS SUITED TO PRESIDE OVER YOUR FEDERATION. BUT THERE WERE SO *MANY* PLANETS AND ONLY *ONE* OF ME.

HARDLY CONDUCIVE TO EFFICIENT GOVERNMENT, EVEN *WITH* THE COOPERATION OF ALL THOSE WORLDS.

CAN'T FIND A WEAK SPOT.

KEEP TRYING.

THANKFULLY, MY NEW INVENTION EFFECTIVELY *ELIMINATES* THAT PROBLEM. AND YOUR -- *MY* NEW SHIP WILL ALLOW ME TO ESTABLISH MY OTHERS THROUGHOUT THE FEDERATION.

I HAD HOPED *YOU* WOULD RECOGNIZE THE LOGIC IN MY PLAN AND JOIN ME.

YOUR PLAN IS NOT *WITHOUT* MERIT. PERHAPS IF YOU WOULD EXPLAIN IT MORE FULLY--

--I *WOULD* CONSIDER JOINING YOU.

TELL ME I DIDN'T *HEAR* THAT RIGHT.

SHH...NOW IT'S THE *KEPTAIN'S* TURN.

SPOCK, YOU *TREACHEROUS HALF-BREED!*

THAT IS *ENOUGH*, CAPTAIN! WHO ARE *YOU* TO QUESTION EITHER SPOCK OR MYSELF?

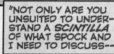

"NOT ONLY ARE YOU UNSUITED TO UNDER-STAND A *SCINTILLA* OF WHAT SPOCK AND I NEED TO DISCUSS--

"--YOU CAN'T *POSSIBLY* FATHOM THE PRESSURES WE ENDURED. ALWAYS OUTSIDERS -- HE A HUMAN ON VULCAN, MYSELF UNWANTED BY MY OWN *PARENTS!*

"YET, WE BOTH PERSEVERED -- *FLOURISHED* -- TO BECOME WHAT WE ARE TODAY."

ARRRRRRRRRR

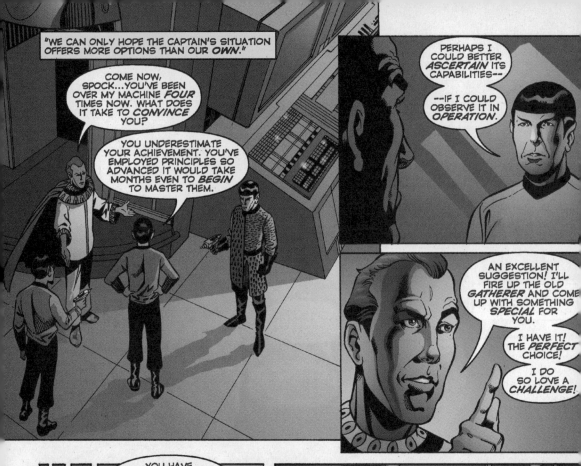

"WE CAN ONLY HOPE THE CAPTAIN'S SITUATION OFFERS MORE OPTIONS THAN OUR *OWN*."

COME NOW, SPOCK...YOU'VE BEEN OVER MY MACHINE *FOUR* TIMES NOW. WHAT DOES IT TAKE TO *CONVINCE* YOU?

YOU UNDERESTIMATE YOUR ACHIEVEMENT. YOU'VE EMPLOYED PRINCIPLES SO ADVANCED IT WOULD TAKE MONTHS EVEN TO *BEGIN* TO MASTER THEM.

PERHAPS I COULD BETTER *ASCERTAIN* ITS CAPABILITIES--

--IF I COULD OBSERVE IT IN *OPERATION*.

AN EXCELLENT SUGGESTION! I'LL FIRE UP THE OLD *GATHERER* AND COME UP WITH SOMETHING *SPECIAL* FOR YOU.

I HAVE IT! THE *PERFECT* CHOICE!

I DO SO LOVE A *CHALLENGE!*

YOU HAVE CLEARLY OVERCOME *MANY* OF THEM ALREADY. IT'S DIFFICULT TO IMAGINE KLINGON *AND* ROMULAN VARIANTS WILLING TO OBEY THE ORDERS OF A *HUMAN*.

INDEED, THE COMPLEXITY OF FINDING VARIANTS OF *YOURSELF* SO EAGER TO EMBRACE YOUR PERSONAL VISION OF OUR UNIVERSE IS NOTHING SHORT OF *STAGGERING*...

IT'S AS IF YOU WERE NOT *GATHERING* ALTERNATE VERSIONS OF YOURSELF, BUT *CREATING* THEM AS YOU WOULD *WISH* THEM TO BE.

BUT I *CAN* DO AS I SAY... AS THIS NEWEST ARRIVAL SO APTLY *PROVES*.

WE MUST BE RUNNING OUT OF *AIR* IN HERE.

THAT *CAN'T* BE WHAT I THINK IT IS.

GULP

YOUR NEW ARRIVAL. IT IS *DOUBTFUL* THAT IN ANY REALITY, *DOCILITY* WOULD BE AN ATTRIBUTE FOUND IN A STARSHIP CAPTAIN.

STILL, IF SUCH A UNIVERSE *DID* EXIST, HOW WAS YOUR DEVICE ABLE TO FUNCTION AT *ALL*--

--GIVEN THAT WHILE EXAMINING IT BUT *MOMENTS* AGO--

"-- I REMOVED THE *COMPUTER* NODULES WHICH CONNECTED IT TO AND REGULATED ITS *POWER* SOURCE."

TAKE HIM! PUT HIM BACK IN HIS PRISON!

WHA-

AGGHH!

UHHHH

I AM SORRY, ARMAND, BUT YOUR REACTION *WAS* PREDICTABLE. ORDER YOUR GUARDS TO DROP THEIR WEAPONS AND FREE MY SHIPMATES.

I *WILL* USE THIS DISRUPTOR ON YOU.

DO WHAT HE SAYS.

GOOD WORK, SPOCK. HOW DID YOU *KNOW?*

AT THE RISK OF SOUNDING AS SELF-IMPORTANT AS ST. JOHN, CAPTAIN, I FIRST SUSPECTED BECAUSE THERE WERE NO *VULCAN* REPLICAS OF MY OLD CLASS-MATE.

DESPITE HIS PROFESSED FRIENDSHIP FOR ME, I BELIEVE ST. JOHN ACTUALLY *FEARS* VULCANS.

"WE REPRESENT A THREAT TO HIS VIEW OF PERSONAL *SUPERIORITY.*"

THAT THERE WERE NO VULCAN ST. JOHNS IN THIS SCIENTIFIC *RESEARCH* CENTER LED ME TO BELIEVE SOMEONE ELSE SUPPLIED ARMAND WITH OTHERS MADE TO FIT HIS DISTORTED VIEW OF *REALITY.*

OH, PLEASE!

"SOMEONE *ELSE,* SPOCK?

THE GENETIC ENGINEERING NECESSARY TO FABRICATE SO *MANY* ALIEN ST. JOHNS IS BEYOND EVEN *HIS* ABILITIES. HIS FRAUDULENT DEVICE LENDS *FURTHER* CREDENCE TO MY BELIEF.

THERE IS SOME UNKNOWN BEING OR POWER AT WORK HERE. IT IS THE ONLY *LOGICAL* CONCLUSION.

THE GATHERING APPARATUS IS A FRAUD. IT DOES NOT WORK. IT HAS *NEVER* WORKED.

NOOOOOOOOOOOO

WHA--WHAT'S *HAPPENING?*

SPOCK.

HOW IS THIS--

THEY--THEY JUST VANISHED! ALL OF THEM.

NOT QUITE *ALL* OF THEM, MR. SULU.

NOW WHERE DID WE PUT THAT *PLANK?*

GULP

NOOOOOOOOOOOO

SOB

"CAPTAIN'S LOG, STARDATE 6620.2: THE ENTERPRISE IS LEAVING POLLUX II, HAVING DOWNLOADED ARMAND ST. JOHN'S FILES IN THE HOPE OF FINDING SOMETHING, *ANYTHING*, ABOUT THE POWER THAT TOOK HOLD OF HIM THERE.

"ST. JOHN HIMSELF WILL NOT BE *ABLE* TO ASSIST US."

"IT IS AS IF HIS MIND DRIFTS AMONG THE SHADOW UNIVERSES THAT EXIST ONLY FOR *HIM*."

I'VE ARRANGED FOR HIS *TRANSFER* TO ELBA II. THEY'VE GOT THE BEST PSYCHIATRIC FACILITIES IN THE *FEDERATION*.

I HOPE *THEY* CAN DO SOMETHING FOR HIM.

YOU GO AHEAD WITHOUT ME. I THINK I'M GOING TO STAY WITH MY *PATIENT* FOR A BIT.

THANK YOU, DOCTOR.

I'M PUTTING SCOTTY IN FOR A *COMMENDATION*. REWRITING THE SHIP'S FUNCTIONS WITH A NEW PROGRAMMING LANGUAGE WAS *INSPIRED*.

STARFLEET SHOULD EQUIP *ALL* OF ITS SHIPS WITH SIMILAR CODES. MAYBE EVEN *VOICE* ACTIVATED.

YOU SEEM SOMEWHAT *DISTRACTED*, MR. SPOCK.

CHECK.

MY APOLOGIES, CAPTAIN. I WAS CONTEMPLATING THE POWER *BEHIND* ARMAND'S MEGALOMANIAC CHARADE.

OUR *SENSORS* DETECTED NOTHING ON THE PLANET. THAT PLUS STARFLEET'S *QUARANTINE* OF POLLUX II SHOULD KEEP WHATEVER WAS THERE OFF OUR BACKS.

I WISH I COULD *AGREE*...

BUT ANYTHING THAT TOOK SO FORCEFUL AN INTEREST IN OUR AFFAIRS ONCE IS ALMOST CERTAIN TO DO SO *AGAIN*.

NOT A VERY *PLEASANT* THOUGHT, MR. SPOCK.

INDEED.

SPOCK...

I COMMEND THEE, SPOCK AND KIRK, FOR A GAME WELL PLAYED.

WHAT DO YOU *TAKE* US FOR, DJINN? WE...*BEAT* YOU...AND ALL YOUR *POSTURING* CAN'T CHANGE THAT!

BUT, SUPPOSE, CAPTAIN, THERE WAS A REMOTE COLONY JUST *BEYOND* WHERE YOU CAPTURED THE ORION SHIP.

A COLONY ON THE VERGE OF A DISCOVERY SO GREAT IT COULD ADVANCE MANKIND ON A HIGH *EVOLUTIONARY* SCALE.

GRANTING YOUR KIND POWER TO RIVAL MY OWN.

HOW BETTER TO THWART THE THREAT THAN TO ATTEND TO IT *BEFORE* IT ARISES?

HOW BETTER TO *AVOID* INTERFERENCE THAN BY INSURING THY SHIP WAS ELSEWHERE AT THE TIME OF GREATEST *NEED*?

THINK ABOUT THAT...

...UNTIL NEXT WE MEET.

CAPTAIN, WE'VE JUST RECEIVED AN EMERGENCY DISTRESS CALL FROM LEORA IV!

BUT THE MESSAGE IS ALREADY STARTING TO *BREAK UP!*

SET COURSE FOR LEORA IV!

BEST POSSIBLE SPEED!

LIEUTENANT?

THE SIGNAL. IT JUST...STOPPED. I'M NOT GETTING ANYTHING NOW.

THERE'S *NOTHING* THERE.

MAINTAIN COURSE AND SPEED, LIEUTENANT.

ASSEMBLE SEARCH AND RESCUE TEAMS.

I'LL BE THERE MOMENTARILY.

"*PERSONAL LOG, SPOCK, STARDATE 6620.4:* WE COULD FIND NO SURVIVORS AT LEORA IV. I HAVE BEEN ATTEMPTING TO UNDERSTAND WHY THIS DJINN POSSESSES SO *POWERFUL* A HATRED OF HUMANITY.

"I HAVE FORMULATED A HYPOTHESIS...

"HIS...PEOPLE...ARE LIKELY UNIMAGINABLY OLD, PERHAPS *ALREADY* IN THEIR DESCENT. I BELIEVE DJINN FEARS HUMANITY WILL SOMEDAY *SURPASS* HIS OWN KIND.

NCC-1701

"AS AN ANCIENT EARTH PHILOSOPHER ONCE ASKED, 'WHAT DID THE *LAST* NEANDERTHAL SAY TO THE *FIRST* CRO-MAGNON?'

"PERHAPS *NOTHING* WAS SAID. PERHAPS THE NEANDERTHAL SIMPLY STRUCK OUT IN ABJECT *TERROR*...

"...OF THAT WHICH WOULD *REPLACE* IT."

UNTIL NEXT WE MEET.

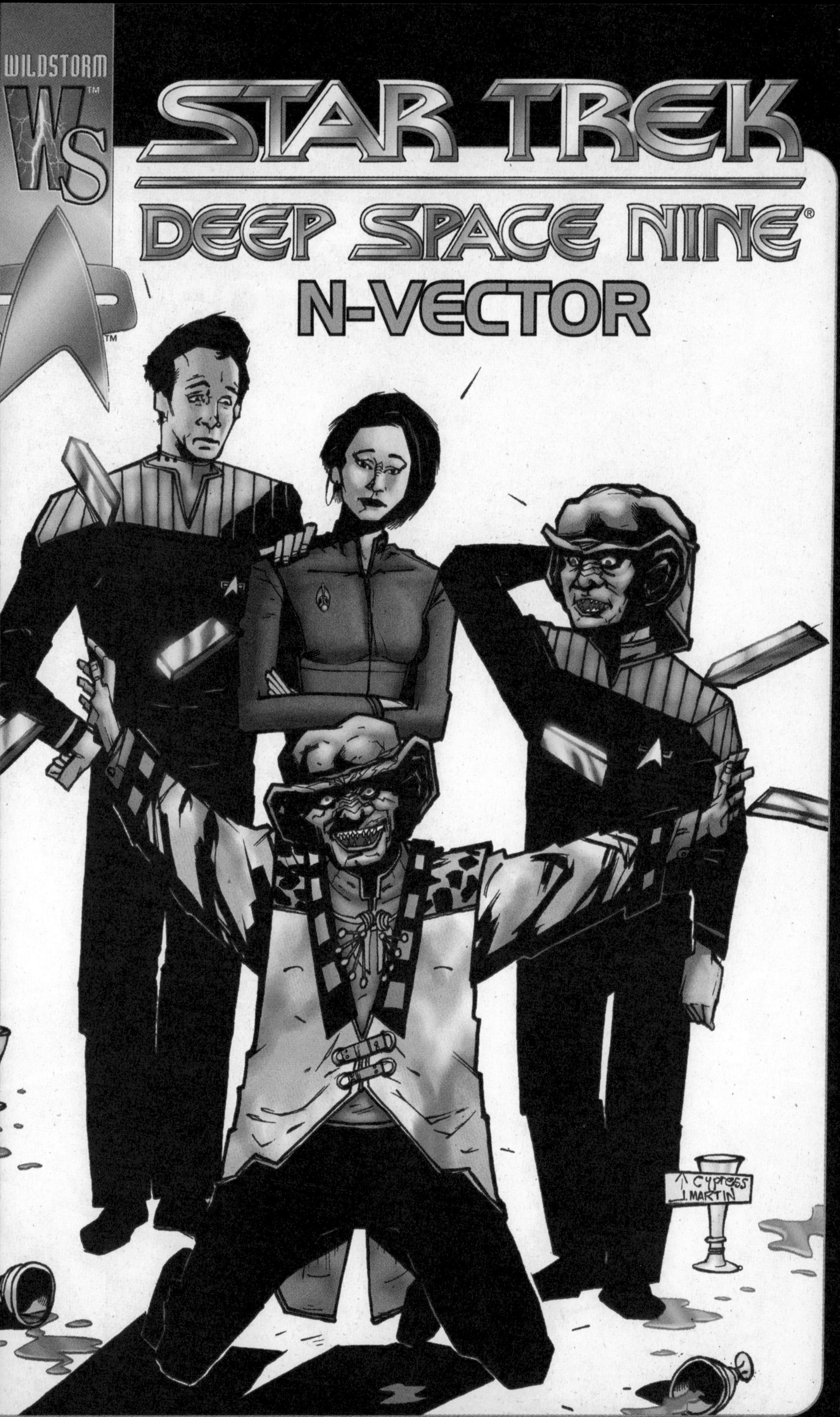
WILDSTORM
WS
STAR TREK
DEEP SPACE NINE®
N-VECTOR
Cypress
J. MARTIN

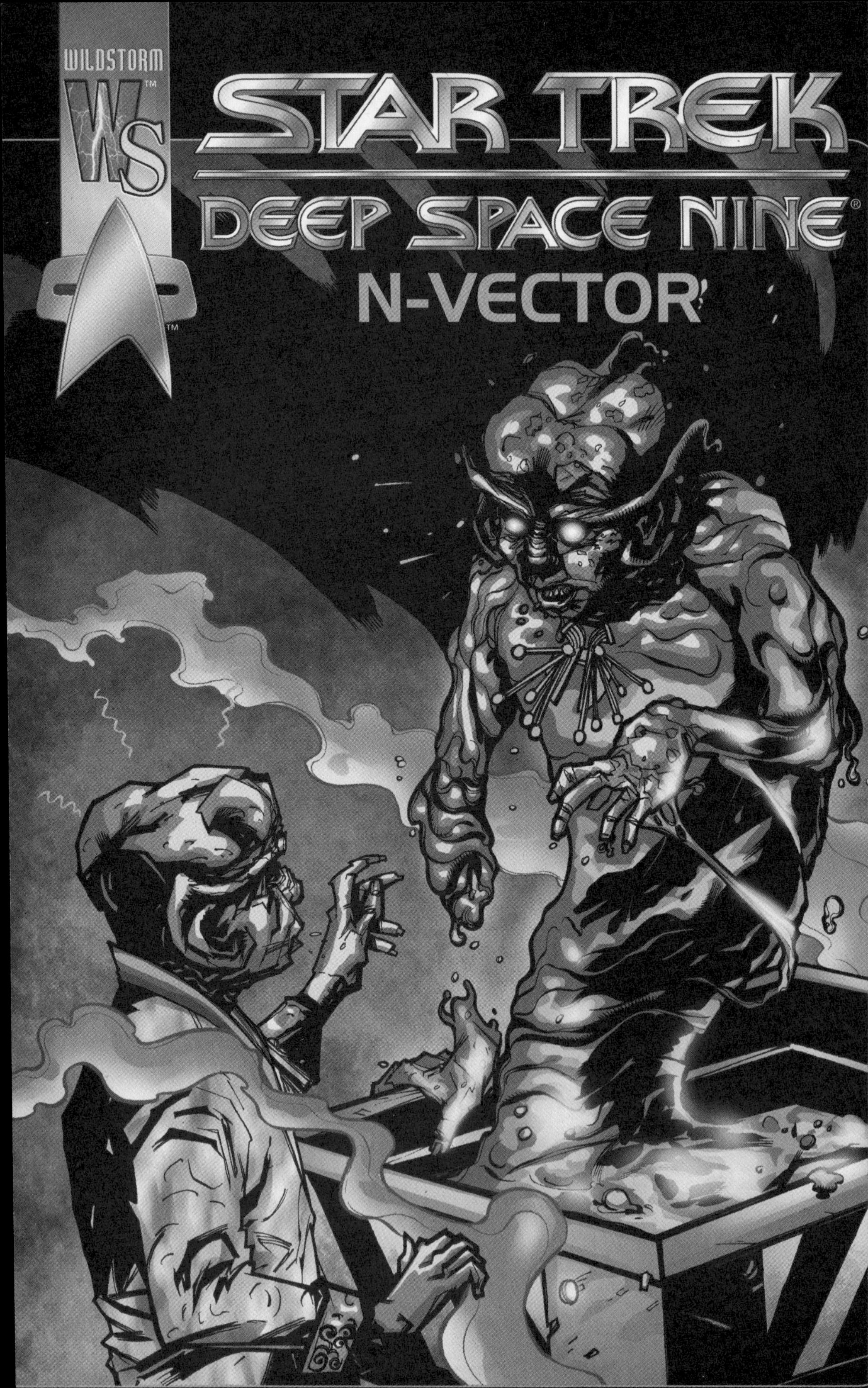
WILDSTORM
STAR TREK
DEEP SPACE NINE
N-VECTOR

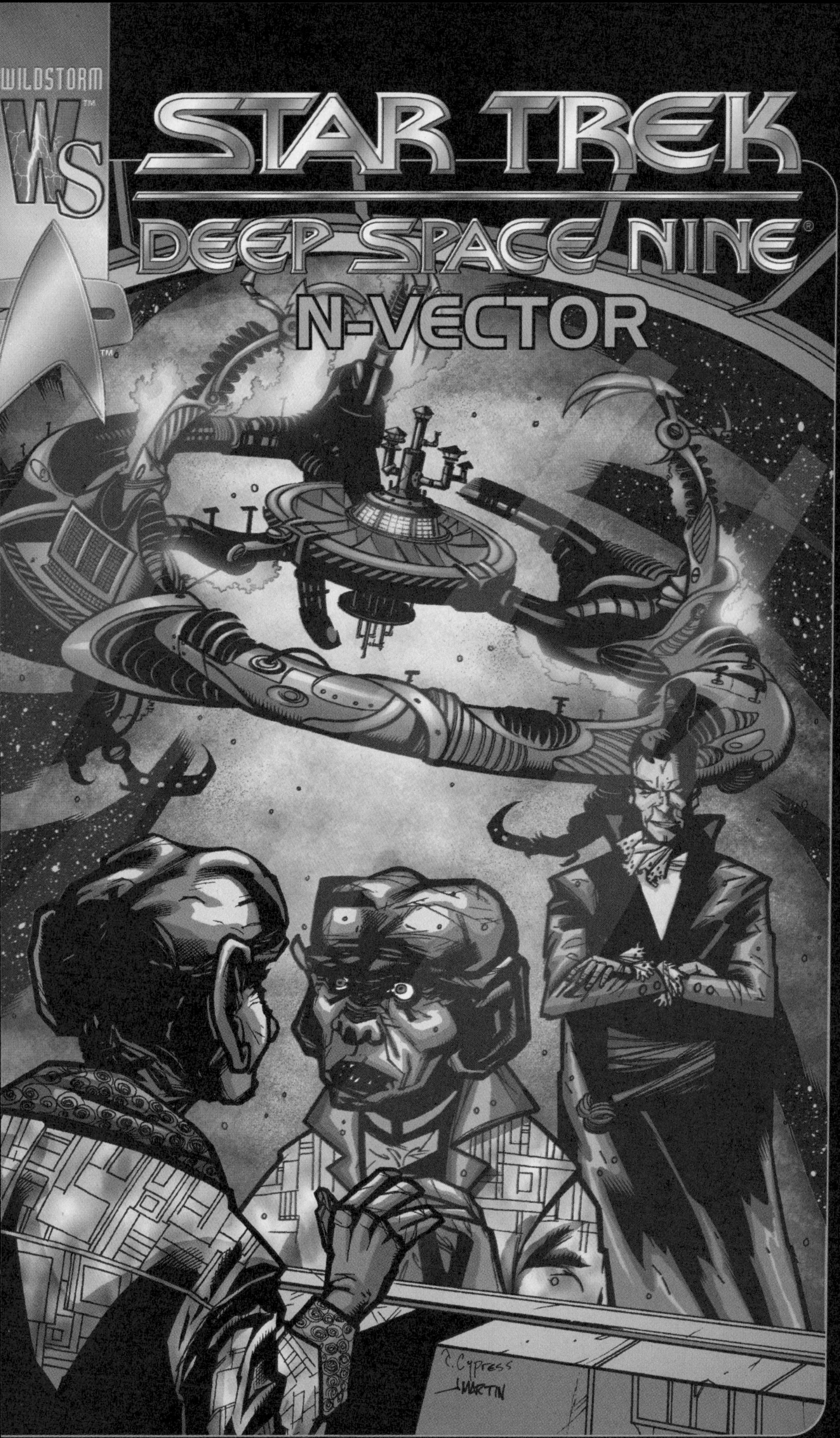
WILDSTORM
STAR TREK
DEEP SPACE NINE
N-VECTOR
C. Cypress
J. MARTIN

PARAMOUNT COMICS®

"DRINKS ARE ON THE HOUSE..."

PRESENTS

K. W. JETER	WRITER
TOBY CYPRESS	PENCILS
MARTIN & IRWIN	INKS
NAGHMEH ZAND	LETTERS
DAN BROWN & BAD@SS & WILDSTORM FX	COLORS
JEFF MARIOTTE	EDITS

STAR TREK: DEEP SPACE NINE®

N - VECTOR

CHAPTER 1

BASED ON STAR TREK: DEEP SPACE NINE®

ALL YOU WANT... ABSOLUTELY FREE...

DRINK UP! ENJOY YOURSELVES! *BE MY GUEST!*

MUST BE SOME KIND A TRICK –

MUST BE.

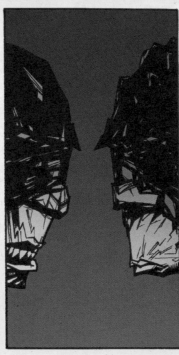

I KNOW THINGS ARE PRETTY *HECTIC* RIGHT NOW, COLONEL KIRA — BUT I WOULDN'T HAVE WANTED YOU TO SEE THIS IF I DIDN'T THINK IT WAS *IMPORTANT*.

I KNOW, LIEUTENANT...

BUT YOU'RE REALLY DOING MORE THAN I EXPECTED YOU TO TAKE ON, WHEN I APPOINTED YOU ACTING CHIEF OF SECURITY. A *LOT* MORE. BUT THERE'S NO WAY YOU'RE GOING TO REPLACE ODO.

I UNDERSTAND —

BELIEVE ME, I'LL BE *HAPPY* TO LET A REAL CHIEF OF SECURITY TAKE OVER.

BUT IN THE MEANTIME —

YOU'VE GOT SOMETHING TO SHOW ME.

YOU SEE THAT, COLONEL? EVERY BLADE OF THE EPS EXHAUST PORT HAS BEEN WEAKENED BY GAMMA-WELD TRACKS, RIGHT UP TO LOAD-COLLAPSE POINT. *AND ALL AT EXACTLY THE SAME ANGLE.*

IF THIS CHAMBER HAD BEEN BROUGHT BACK ONLINE BEFORE THIS HAD BEEN DISCOVERED —

THEN WE WOULD HAVE BEEN IN A REACTION OVERLOAD SITUATION — WITH NO WAY OF SHUTTING THIS CHAMBER DOWN, EITHER AUTOMATICALLY *OR* MANUALLY.

HOW MANY OTHER SYSTEM FAILURES LIKE THIS HAVE TURNED UP?

FIFTY-SIX... AND COUNTING. ALL THROUGH THE STATION —

THAT'S NOT GOOD...

NOT GOOD FOR *SOMEBODY.*

SO WHO ELSE HAVE YOU TALKED TO ABOUT THIS?

NO ONE, COLONEL. EVEN THE STATION ENGINEERS DON'T KNOW ABOUT ALL OF IT.

KEEP IT THAT WAY. AND I WANT A FULL REPORT, ON MY DESK —

IN THIRTEEN HOURS.

YES, SIR!

LT. NOG —

I THINK THERE'S SOMETHING ELSE THAT THE HEAD OF SECURITY NEEDS TO TAKE A LOOK AT. RIGHT NOW.

THERE BETTER NOT BE ANY MORE PROBLEMS, BECAUSE I'VE GOT ENOUGH OF THEM.

ANY WORD FROM THE *DEFIANT*?

NOT YET, SIR.

GREAT. IF STARFLEET WANTS TO KEEP THEIR SHIP DETAILED TO THIS STATION, THEY COULD AT LEAST HAVE SENT IT TO FETCH A NEW COMMANDER WHO KNOWS HOW TO BE PUNCTUAL.

WHAT'S GOING ON HERE?

LOOKS LIKE QUARK'S GONE CRAZY —

BUT IN A *GOOD* WAY.

COLONEL — WE'VE GOT A SHIP APPROACHING.

IF THAT'S THE *DEFIANT*, TELL ITS COMMANDER JAST THAT I WANT TO SPEAK TO HER. IMMEDIATELY.

NEGATIVE, SIR — IT'S A *ROMULAN* SHUTTLE. TRAVELING UNDER A *DIPLOMATIC* PASS.

DIPLOMATIC? WHO'S ON BOARD IT?

ACCORDING TO THE INFORMATION TRANSMITTED SO FAR, THE PASS IS CREDENTIALED TO A ROMULAN XENOBIO-LOGICAL RESEARCHER NAMED MOS SENAY.

I *SAID* I DIDN'T NEED ANY MORE PROBLEMS!

AN INTEREST-FREE LOAN? ON NO COLLATERAL? NO PROBLEM!

AN HONEST FACE LIKE YOURS IS ALL THE COLLATERAL I NEED —

UNCLE QUARK! WHAT'RE YOU *DOING*?

WHAT AM I DOING? I'M DOING BUSINESS, OF COURSE!

BUT... BUT... GIVING AWAY DRINKS? MAKING LOANS YOU'LL NEVER GET PAID BACK?

WHAT ABOUT THE FERENGI RULES OF ACQUISITION?

THE FERENGI RULES OF ACQUISITION ARE *NOT* THE LAST WORD IN BUSINESS.

IN FACT... THEY'RE OUTDATED.

YOU SEE, THERE ARE *NEW* WAYS OF DOING BUSINESS NOW... *NEW* IDEAS! NEW CONCEPTS! IT'S NOT IMPORTANT TO MAKE MONEY –

IT'S NOT?

OF COURSE NOT! WHAT'S IMPORTANT IS TO BUILD *MARKET SHARE.* AND YOU HAVE TO SPEND MONEY TO DO THAT! YOU HAVE TO *BUY* YOUR CUSTOMERS...

... SO YOU SEE, IN THE NEW WAY OF DOING BUSINESS, MONEY ISN'T IMPORTANT. IT'S WORTHLESS! THE ONLY THING THAT MATTERS IS MAKING SURE THAT YOUR CUSTOMER KNOWS THAT YOU'RE HIS *FRIEND.*

YOU'RE SCARING ME.

NOG, THIS IS COLONEL KIRA. I NEED YOU IMMEDIATELY AT CARGO BAY TWELVE—

DON'T GO ANYWHERE, ALL RIGHT? JUST STAY HERE.

WHY SHOULD I GO ANYWHERE ELSE?

BUSINESS IS GREAT!

WHAT'S HAPPENING? I HEARD THERE WAS SOMETHING GOING ON HERE...

LOOK AFTER HIM, WILL YOU? I THINK IT'S SERIOUS!

WHAT ARE YOU TALKING ABOUT?

OH.

HOLD IT RIGHT THERE.

COLONEL KIRA — HOW PLEASANT TO SEE YOU AGAIN.

I DOUBT IT. ESPECIALLY SINCE I'M ABOUT TO TELL YOUR CREW TO HAUL THAT STUFF BACK ABOARD YOUR SHIP, AND OFF MY STATION.

THAT WON'T BE *POSSIBLE*, COLONEL. YOU'D BETTER TAKE ANOTHER LOOK AT MY DIPLOMATIC PASS —

YOU'LL SEE THAT IT EXPRESSLY ORDERS YOU TO FACILITATE THE TRANSFER OF BOTH MYSELF *AND* MY EQUIPMENT ABOARD DS9.

YOUR FEDERATION AND THE ROMULAN EMPIRE ARE *ALLIES* NOW. THERE'S NOTHING YOU CAN *DO* ABOUT IT.

I WASN'T HAPPY ABOUT IT A YEAR AGO, WHEN YOU *FIRST* SHOWED UP HERE. AND I *REALLY* WASN'T HAPPY WHEN STARFLEET LET YOU SEAL OFF AN ENTIRE SUBSECTION FOR YOUR SO-CALLED LABORATORY —

AND I TAKE IT THAT THE SEAL IS STILL IN PLACE? I'D HATE TO THINK THAT YOU MIGHT HAVE DIS-OBEYED STARFLEET'S DIRECT ORDERS.

YOUR LAB IS STILL THERE WAITING, SENAY. JUST LIKE *I'M* GOING TO BE WAITING UNTIL I CAN BOOT YOU *OFF* DS9. FOR *GOOD*.

KEEP AN *EYE* ON HIM.

I DID YOU A FAVOR...

I KEPT A TALLY OF ALL THE NO-INTEREST, NO-COLLATERAL *LOANS* THAT YOU MADE.

OHHH...

QUARK! *QUARK* —

NOG, THIS IS DOCTOR BASHIR. I'VE GOT QUARK IN THE STATION *INFIRMARY*. HE'S OKAY FOR NOW, BUT I'M GOING TO BE GIVING HIM A THOROUGH *EXAMINATION*.

THANKS. I'LL CHECK WITH YOU LATER ABOUT HIM —

I'VE GOT SOME OTHER THINGS TO TAKE CARE OF.

I CAN'T BELIEVE IT...

I CAN'T BELIEVE IT...

I'M SORRY... BUT THAT'S WHAT MY INVESTIGATION TURNED UP. ALL THE INSTANCES OF DELIBERATE DAMAGE POINT TO *ONE PERSON*.

'DELIBERATE DAMAGE'... YOU'RE TALKING *SABOTAGE*. THAT'S A SERIOUS *CHARGE* TO MAKE.

ALL RIGHT. I'LL TAKE IT FROM HERE.

WILL YOU BE CONTACTING STARFLEET INTERNAL AFFAIRS?

I DON'T KNOW YET. I'LL HAVE TO THINK ABOUT IT.

DISMISSED.

A WORD WITH YOU, COLONEL KIRA...

WHAT DO *YOU* WANT?

ONLY TO HELP.

YOU'D HELP ME IF YOU JUST WENT BACK TO YOUR SEALED-OFF LAB SECTOR AND STAYED OUT OF MY PROBLEMS.

BUT YOUR PROBLEMS *ARE* MY PROBLEMS...

YOU SEE, COLONEL, I KNOW ALL ABOUT WHAT'S BEEN HAPPENING ON THIS STATION. AND ABOUT THE DAMAGE INCIDENTS THAT YOUR ACTING HEAD OF SECURITY HAS BEEN INVESTIGATING.

I KNOW MORE ABOUT THEM THAN *YOU* DO.

LET ME PUT THIS TO YOU STRAIGHT, SENAY. I DON'T *LIKE* YOU BEING ABOARD DS9. I DON'T KNOW WHAT YOU'RE *DOING* HERE, OR WHAT YOUR *RESEARCH* PROJECT IS ABOUT – BUT I DON'T LIKE HAVING YOU SHOVED DOWN OUR *THROATS*.

SO STAY OUT OF MY BUSINESS, OR I'LL *FIND* A WAY TO GET YOU OFF THE STATION. UNDERSTOOD?

PERFECTLY, COLONEL.

BUT WE'LL TALK AGAIN...

DELAYED? FOR WHAT REASON?

I'M SORRY, SIR; THE COMMUNICATION FROM THE DEFIANT DIDN'T SAY.

MAYBE IT'S JUST AS WELL...

ONE LESS THING TO DEAL WITH RIGHT NOW.

YOU RELEASED HIM? YOU LET QUARK GO?

I HAD TO...

I GAVE HIM A COMPLETE BATTERY OF PSYCHOLOGICAL TESTS. THE *WORKS.*

AND WHAT DID YOU FIND?

ACCORDING TO THE RESULTS I GOT, QUARK IS A BORDERLINE SOCIOPATH, WITH SEVERELY IMPAIRED MORAL FUNCTIONING, AND OBSESSED TO THE POINT OF MONOMANIA WITH NOTHING BUT PROFITS.

IN OTHER WORDS...

HE'S A NORMAL FERENGI.

YES, AND A *BROKE* FERENGI, TOO!

I'VE BARELY GOT ENOUGH LEFT TO KEEP THIS PLACE OPEN...

ALL THE DAMAGE... ALL THOSE FREE DRINKS... AND THOSE *LOANS!* I'M RUINED!

OH, COME ON NOW - IT'S ONLY *MONEY.*

ONLY MONEY? THAT'S *ENOUGH!* AND BESIDES - IT'S *NOT* JUST MONEY...

WHAT IS IT, THEN?

IT'S MY *REPUTATION!* HOW AM I GOING TO HOLD MY HEAD UP AROUND OTHER FERENGIS, WHEN THEY FIND OUT... WHEN THEY FIND OUT...

THAT I *GAVE* THINGS AWAY...

I'M *TOTALLY* RUINED.

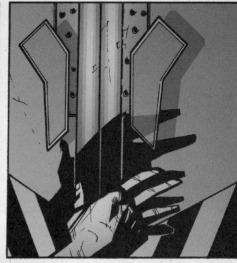

THE RESULTS SHOULD BE *INTERESTING.*

RESEARCH NOTES, SEGMENT BETA TWELVE. THE *VIROID* HAS PENETRATED ITS TARGET HOST EVEN MORE DEEPLY THAN I HAD *ANTICIPATED...*

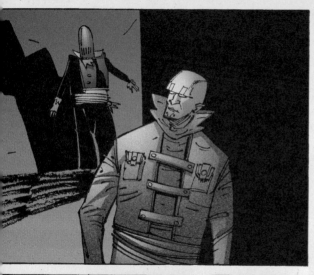

WHO'S *THERE*?

YOU OWE QUARK MONEY.

YEAH? SO WHAT'S IT TO YOU?

IT'S ENOUGH.

WILL YOU BE ALL RIGHT?

OH, SURE. IT'S LIKE THAT OLD SAYING - *TOMORROW IS ANOTHER DAY.*

I DON'T REMEMBER THAT FROM THE FERENGI RULES OF ACQUISITION...

OH, JUST GO *AWAY*...

... ROTTEN CHEATS... TAKING *ADVANTAGE* OF A DISHONEST MAN LIKE THAT...

WHAT THE -

"THIS ONE IS PAID IN FULL..."

"*MORE TO COME.*"

BRRING!

I'M SURE GLAD THAT KEIKO AND THE KIDS AREN'T HERE TO SEE THIS MESS...

YES?

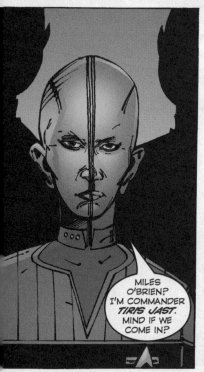

MILES O'BRIEN? I'M COMMANDER *TIRIS JAST.* MIND IF WE COME IN?

IS YOUR WIFE HERE?

NO – I SENT HER AND OUR CHILDREN OFF ON A LITTLE VACATION, WHILE I GOT US SETTLED IN HERE.

LOOK, WHAT'S THIS ALL *ABOUT?* I START TEACHING CLASSES AT THE ACADEMY ON MONDAY--

DON'T WORRY ABOUT YOUR CLASSES — THEY'VE BEEN *CANCELLED*. AND WE'LL BE IN TOUCH WITH YOUR *WIFE*, SO SHE'LL KNOW WHERE YOU'VE *GONE*.

WHAT ARE YOU *TALKING* ABOUT? I'M NOT *GOING* ANYWHERE.

YOU KNOW, THIS ISN'T THE KIND OF THING THAT A SHIP'S COMMANDER USUALLY TAKES CARE OF. BUT STARFLEET INTERNAL AFFAIRS ASKED ME TO ASSIST. AND —

I JUST WANTED TO GET A *LOOK* AT YOU.

SECURE HIM, AND LET'S *GO*.

YOU WON'T BE TEACHING ANY CLASSES AT THE *ACADEMY*, O'BRIEN. YOU'RE GOING BACK TO DS9.

TO FACE CHARGES —

OF *SABOTAGE*.

I *MISSED* ONE...

COLONEL, THIS IS DOCTOR BASHIR. WE'VE RECEIVED THE LAST OF THE CASUALTIES HERE IN THE INFIRMARY. ONE DEATH; PROGNOSIS STABLE TO GOOD ON THE OTHERS.

THANKS.

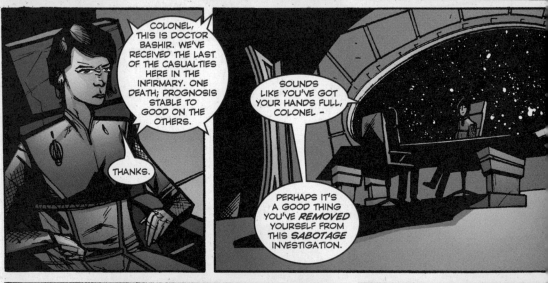

SOUNDS LIKE YOU'VE GOT YOUR HANDS FULL, COLONEL -

PERHAPS IT'S A GOOD THING YOU'VE *REMOVED* YOURSELF FROM THIS *SABOTAGE* INVESTIGATION.

LET'S GET THIS *STRAIGHT,* JAST. THE INVESTIGATION OF OUR FORMER OPS CHIEF MILES O'BRIEN IS *DS9* BUSINESS NOW. YOU'VE DONE *YOUR* JOB, BRINGING HIM BACK HERE.

THE REST DOESN'T *CONCERN* YOU.

I *KNOW* O'BRIEN IS INNOCENT OF THESE SABOTAGE CHARGES. WHEN STARFLEET INTERNAL AFFAIRS FINDS THAT OUT -

NOBODY IS GOING TO BE ABLE TO SAY I INFLUENCED THEIR VERDICT.

THE *DEFIANT* HASN'T BEEN DETAILED TO DS9 JUST SO I CAN SIT BACK AND WATCH THE STATION FALL APART.

EVERYTHING THAT GOES ON HERE CONCERNS ME.

WE'VE JUST SEEN THE *RESULTS* OF SOME OF THAT SABOTAGE. IF YOUR FRIEND O'BRIEN IS RESPONSIBLE — HE'LL *PAY*.

AND IF YOU DON'T GET THIS WHOLE MESS CLEANED UP — AND *SOON* — STARFLEET MAY BEGIN WONDERING IF YOU'RE THE RIGHT PERSON TO BE RUNNING THIS STATION.

LT. NOG — I WANT A FULL *REPORT* ON THIS SABOTAGE INCIDENT. IN THE COMMANDER'S OFFICE, IN *ONE* HOUR.

UNTIL THEN, I'VE GOT SOME OTHER BUSINESS TO TAKE CARE OF.

WELL, COLONEL KIRA — WHAT A PLEASANT SURPRISE. WHAT BRINGS YOU —

CUT IT, QUARK. I WOULD HAVE SENT MY ACTING SECURITY CHIEF HERE TO TALK TO YOU, BUT HE'S *BUSY* RIGHT NOW.

YOU MEAN MY NEPHEW NOG?

NOG'S A GOOD LAD, EVEN THOUGH HE HAS BEEN CORRUPTED WITH ALL THESE CRAZY NOTIONS OF *DUTY* AND *RESPONSIBILITY* —

I'M NOT HERE TO TALK ABOUT NOG. I'M HERE TO FIND OUT WHAT'S GOING ON.

'GOING ON?' WHAT DO YOU MEAN?

I MEAN THIS LITTLE LOAN-SHARKING BUSINESS YOU SEEM TO HAVE STARTED UP HERE ON DS9. *THAT'S* WHAT.

LOAN-SHARKING? YOU MUST BE CRAZY –

NOT THAT I CONSIDER LOAN-SHARKING TO BE ANYTHING OTHER THAN A TIME-HONORED AND RESPECTABLE FERENGI LINE OF *BUSINESS*.

BUT I'M NOT DOING ANYTHING LIKE THAT. I'VE GOT A BAR TO RUN.

REALLY? THEN TELL ME WHY DOCTOR BASHIR HAS CLOSE TO A *DOZEN* INDIVIDUALS IN THE STATION *INFIRMARY*, WHO WERE BEATEN WITHIN AN INCH OF THEIR LIVES –

AND WHO ALL OWED YOU MONEY.

HMMM...

COINCIDENCE?

IT'S NOT GOING TO BE COINCIDENCE, QUARK, WHEN I HAVE MY ACTING SECURITY CHIEF PULL YOUR *OPERATING LICENSE* FOR THIS ESTABLISHMENT.

I DON'T KNOW WHA YOU THINK YOU'R DOING, QUARK, BL THIS IS ONE BUSINES YOU'RE *NOT* GOIN TO BE RUNNING C MY STATION. YO EITHER SHUT DOWN –

OR I'LL SHUT *YOU* DOWN. GOT IT?

... SEE WHAT I CAN DO, COLONEL.

YOU'VE GOT A VISITOR.

HELLO, MILES.

GOOD OF YOU TO DROP BY, JULIAN. I HAVEN'T SEEN A *FRIENDLY* FACE IN A WHILE.

IT'S NOT ENTIRELY A SOCIAL CALL —

I'M PART OF THE TEAM INVESTIGATING THE CHARGES OF SABOTAGE THAT HAVE BEEN BROUGHT AGAINST YOU.

YOU'RE INVESTIGATING ME? BUT, JULIAN —

YOU KNOW THESE CHARGES ARE *IMPOSSIBLE!*

I WOULD *NEVER* HAVE DONE ANYTHING TO SABOTAGE DS9!

I DON'T 'KNOW' ANYTHING, MILES. I HAVE TO KEEP AN OPEN *MIND* ABOUT ALL OF THIS.

THAT'S THE ONLY WAY I'M GOING TO BE ABLE TO *HELP* YOU.

ALL WE KNOW SO FAR IS THAT THERE APPEARS TO HAVE BEEN A WIDESPREAD CAMPAIGN OF *SABOTAGE* THROUGHOUT THE STATION'S MAJOR *OPERATIONS* SYSTEMS. ONE OF THE FUSION REACTION CHAMBERS FAILED JUST AFTER YOU WERE BROUGHT BACK HERE — AND A MAN *DIED* BECAUSE OF IT.

BUT WHAT'S THAT GOT TO DO WITH *ME?*

ALL OF THE SABOTAGE CAN BE TRACED BACK TO WHEN YOU WERE THE STATION'S OPS CHIEF. YOU WERE THE ONLY ONE WHO *COULD* HAVE DONE IT.

THAT'S THE WAY IT APPEARS, AT LEAST.

BUT YOU DON'T BELIEVE THAT — DO YOU, JULIAN?

IF I *BELIEVED* IT...

I WOULDN'T HAVE AGREED TO BE PART OF THE INVESTIGATION.

IF I BELIEVED IT... I WOULDN'T HAVE AGREED TO BE PART OF THE INVESTIGATION.

A VERY INTERESTING CONVERSATION, DOCTOR BASHIR.

THAT WAS A *PRIVATE* EXCHANGE BETWEEN MYSELF AND THE ACCUSED. YOU HAD NO *RIGHT* TO LISTEN IN.

ON THE CONTRARY, DOCTOR. I WAS *AUTHORIZED* TO DO SO BY STARFLEET INTERNAL AFFAIRS. THERE'S *MORE* AT STAKE HERE THAN JUST O'BRIEN'S GUILT OR INNOCENCE.

I'M IN CHARGE OF THIS INVESTIGATION — AND I DON'T HAVE ANY SENTIMENTAL *ATTACHMENT* TO *ANYONE* HERE ON DS9. IF O'BRIEN IS FOUND *GUILTY*, THEN ALL OF HIS FORMER ASSOCIATES — INCLUDING YOURSELF, DOCTOR — ARE UNDER SUSPICION AS WELL.

THERE'S A LOT RIDING ON THIS INVESTIGATION — FOR BOTH YOU *AND* YOUR FRIEND O'BRIEN.

SO WHAT ARE YOU GOING TO DO?

WHAT AM I GOING TO DO? I DON'T HAVE ANY *CHOICE*!

I'M GOING TO 'TAKE CARE' OF THE SITUATION.

DO YOU WANT ME TO HELP?

OH, *SURE*! I'M GOING TO ASK THE ACTING CHIEF OF SECURITY FOR HELP!

I'M BEGINNING TO WONDER JUST HOW MUCH *FERENGI* IS LEFT IN YOU.

WANT HIM TO *HELP*... THAT'S A LAUGH, ALL RIGHT...

HOLD IT RIGHT THERE.

IT'S NOT THAT I DON'T APPRECIATE WHAT YOU'VE BEEN DOING - I APPRECIATE *ANYTHING* THAT GETS MY MONEY BACK - BUT YOU'VE GOTTEN ME INTO A LOT OF TROUBLE.

AND I WANT SOME *EXPLANATIONS*.

MY APOLOGIES...

I WAS ONLY TRYING TO *HELP.*

THAT'S FINE - IT'S NOT THAT I DON'T APPRECIATE IT -

BUT WHO ARE YOU? AND WHY HAVE YOU BEEN GOING AROUND COLLECTING THE MONEY THAT'S OWED TO ME?

YOU CAN CALL ME - VIQTOR.

EVERYTHING I'VE DONE... IT'S SO YOU WOULD HAVE *CONFIDENCE* IN ME.

YOU *NEED* TO TRUST ME.

THEN WE CAN DO *BUSINESS* TOGETHER.

YOU DIDN'T SEAL OFF YOUR LAB --

THAT'S BECAUSE I WAS HOPING YOU WOULD CHANGE YOUR *MIND.* ABOUT COMING HERE TO TALK WITH ME.

I ONLY CAME HERE BECAUSE YOU SAID YOU KNEW SOMETHING ABOUT O'BRIEN.

I KNOW MORE THAN THAT, DOCTOR. I KNOW *EVERYTHING* ABOUT YOUR FRIEND O'BRIEN.

AND ABOUT THESE *SABOTAGE* CHARGES AGAINST HIM.

YOUR MESSAGE SAID THAT YOU HAVE *EVIDENCE* THAT WOULD PROVE THAT HE WASN'T *INVOLVED.*

LET'S *HEAR* IT.

I DIDN'T SAY THAT O'BRIEN WASN'T INVOLVED. I SAID THAT HE WASN'T *RESPONSIBLE.*

THERE'S A DIFFERENCE.

O'BRIEN WAS INVOLVED IN THE SABOTAGE, ALL RIGHT -- BUT HE DIDN'T DO IT.

SOMETHING ELSE DID.

THERE WAS A *REASON*, DOCTOR, THAT I CAME TO DS9 FOR MY RESEARCH. IT'S THE PERFECT ENVIRONMENT FOR OBSERVING AN ENTITY KNOWN AS THE N-VECTOR VIROID IN OPERATION.

I'VE NEVER HEARD OF IT.

I'M NOT *SURPRISED*, DOCTOR. ONLY A FEW AT THE HIGHEST LEVELS OF THE ROMULAN GOVERNMENT KNOW ABOUT THE VIROID. IT'S POTENTIALLY ONE OF THE MOST *POWERFUL* THINGS IN THE UNIVERSE. EITHER AS A *TOOL*... OR A *WEAPON*.

JUST WHAT IS THIS... *VIROID* SUPPOSED TO BE?

YOU'RE A SCIENTIFIC MAN, DOCTOR. YOU KNOW HOW A VIRUS WORKS, DON'T YOU?

OF COURSE. A VIRUS IS ALMOST PURE INFORMATION; IT TAKES OVER THE CELLS OF A LIVING CREATURE AND CHANGES THE CELLS' PROGRAMMING FOR ITS OWN PURPOSES. USUALLY JUST TO PROPAGATE ITSELF TO OTHER HOST CREATURES.

THE N-VECTOR VIROID IS UNIQUELY DIFFERENT FROM A MERE VIRUS. IT'S A TRUE - SHALL WE SAY? - *CROSS PLATFORM* INFECTIOUS AGENT.

EXACTLY SO, DOCTOR. BUT A VIRUS IS LIMITED TO INFECTING BIOLOGICAL ORGANISMS - LIVING CREATURES.

THIS VIROID CAN INFECT AND TAKE OVER *ANY* ORGANIZED MATERIAL SUBSTANCE - BIOLOGICAL, MECHANICAL, ELECTRONIC - *ANYTHING!*

DO YOU KNOW WHAT THAT MEANS, DOCTOR?

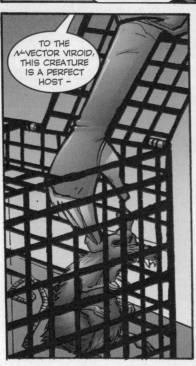

TO THE N-VECTOR VIROID, THIS CREATURE IS A PERFECT HOST -

IT CAN CHANGE THIS CREATURE'S BEHAVIOR HOWEVER IT DESIRES - OR EVEN ITS PHYSICAL SHAPE.

JUST AS THE VIROID CAN INFECT AND CHANGE SOMETHING LIKE *THIS*.

AND SIZE OR COMPLEXITY IS NO BARRIER TO THE VIROID. IT CAN INFECT A MOUSE, OR SOMETHING AS BIG AS –

"DS9 ITSELF."

THAT'S *IMPOSSIBLE* —

AND YET YOU ALSO BELIEVE THAT IT'S 'IMPOSSIBLE' THAT YOUR FRIEND O'BRIEN IS RESPONSIBLE FOR THE SABOTAGE DONE TO THE STATION. IT'S EITHER ONE OR THE OTHER, DOCTOR —

AND IF WHAT I'VE TOLD YOU ABOUT THE *Λ*-VECTOR VIROID ISN'T TRUE, THEN YOU AND YOUR FRIEND ARE IN VERY DEEP TROUBLE *INDEED*.

HOW COULD YOU HAVE DEVELOPED SUCH A THING?

PERHAPS IT WASN'T 'DEVELOPED,' DOCTOR —

"PERHAPS IT ALREADY EXISTED, AND I MERELY *DISCOVERED* IT."

LET'S JUST SAY THAT STARFLEET IS PERHAPS *WISER* THAN IT REALIZES, IN HAVING PLACED A *BAN* ON ENTERING THE GAMMA QUADRANT —

"THERE ARE THINGS IN THERE, WITH POWERS AND INTELLIGENCE THAT YOU COULD BARELY COMPREHEND, DOCTOR."

INTELLIGENCE? YOU TALK OF THIS THING AS IF IT WERE *CONSCIOUS* — AS IF IT WERE SMART ENOUGH TO KNOW WHAT IT'S DOING —

IT'S CONSCIOUS, ALL RIGHT. AND AS TO HOW SMART IT MIGHT BE — THE QUESTION BECOMES —

WHETHER IT'S SMARTER THAN *WE* ARE.

NOW THAT WE TRUST EACH OTHER —

LET ME MAKE YOU A *BUSINESS* PROPOSITION.

ONE THAT WILL BE PROFITABLE FOR BOTH OF US —

PROFITABLE ENOUGH TO WIPE OUT *ALL* YOUR DEBTS — AND MORE.

REALLY? WELL, I'M ALWAYS READY TO DO BUSINESS —

ESPECIALLY WITH SOMEBODY OF *YOUR* OBVIOUS INTELLIGENCE!

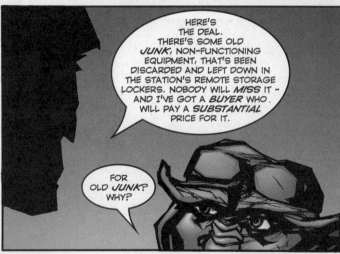

HERE'S THE DEAL. THERE'S SOME OLD *JUNK*, NON-FUNCTIONING EQUIPMENT, THAT'S BEEN DISCARDED AND LEFT DOWN IN THE STATION'S REMOTE STORAGE LOCKERS. NOBODY WILL *MISS* IT — AND I'VE GOT A *BUYER* WHO WILL PAY A *SUBSTANTIAL* PRICE FOR IT.

FOR OLD *JUNK*? WHY?

YOU DON'T NEED TO KNOW *WHY*. YOU JUST NEED TO HELP ME GET THE STUFF WHERE IT HAS TO GO.

ARE YOU WITH ME ON THIS — OR *NOT*?

DO I HAVE A *CHOICE*?

NO.

THEN I GUESS I *AM*.

YOU KNOW – AS A GENERAL RULE, I DON'T BELIEVE IN HEAVY LABOR AS A WAY OF MAKING MONEY.

IT'S ONE OF THE FERENGI RULES OF ACQUISITION: "ALWAYS GET SOMEBODY ELSE TO DO THE *LIFTING*."

STOP COMPLAINING. IT'LL BE *WORTH* YOUR TROUBLE.

BUT I DON'T EVEN KNOW HOW WE'RE GOING TO GET THIS STUFF OFF THE STATION –

COLONEL KIRA HAS PUT A COMPLETE *BAN* ON FLIGHTS LEAVING DS9 UNTIL THIS *SABOTAGE* THING IS ALL CLEARED UP.

LET ME WORRY ABOUT THAT.

WHEN WE'RE READY TO *GO*, WE WON'T HAVE ANY TROUBLE LEAVING HERE.

WAIT A MINUTE – THIS WASN'T IN THE STORAGE LOCKER.

THIS CAME OUT OF THAT SEALED-OFF SUBSECTOR – WHERE THAT ROMULAN XENOBIOLOGIST SET UP HIS LAB!

LET'S GET SOME THINGS *STRAIGHT*.

WE'RE PARTNERS –

BUT THERE ARE JUST SOME THINGS THAT DON'T CONCERN YOU.

UNDERSTAND?

SURE... OF COURSE! NO PROBLEM!

SOME THINGS ARE JUST *PERSONAL*.

"A PARTNERSHIP IS A GOOD THING..."

I PROPOSE A PARTNERSHIP BETWEEN MYSELF –

AND *YOU*, DOCTOR BASHIR.

WHAT DO YOU MEAN?

VERY SIMPLE, DOCTOR. WE *BOTH* HAVE THINGS THAT WE WANT.

YOU WISH TO CLEAR YOU FRIEND O'BRIEN OF SABOTAGE CHARGES –

AND I WANT THE *N*-VECTOR VIROID. UNDER *MY* CONTROL.

DO WE HAVE A DEAL?

PERHAPS.

HOW ARE WE GOING TO MAKE THIS ALL HAPPEN?

AS I SAID BEFORE, DOCTOR, THE VIROID IS SMART. *VERY* SMART.

THAT MEANS IT CAN BE TRICKED.

THE N-VECTOR VIROID EVOLVES BY INFECTING AND TAKING OVER SYSTEMS OF INCREASING COMPLEXITY.

FROM A ONE-CELLED MICRO-ORGANISM TO AN INTELLIGENT BEING SUCH AS YOUR FRIEND O'BRIEN —

AND FROM O'BRIEN TO DS9! IT'S LIKE A *DISEASE* THAT PICKS ITS OWN *TARGETS*!

PRECISELY, DOCTOR.

THE TRICK IS TO GIVE THE VIROID A MORE *TEMPTING* TARGET. ONE THAT IT WOULD *PREFER* TO INFECT, LEAVING ITS PREVIOUS TARGET BEHIND.

THAT'S WHERE *YOU* COME IN.

THE SO-CALLED SABOTAGE, OF WHICH YOUR FRIEND O'BRIEN HAS BEEN ACCUSED, IS NOTHING MORE THAN THE VIROID SEEKING A BETTER, MORE COMPLEX — AND SMARTER — HOST TO INFECT.

THE VIROID ISN'T *STABLE*; IT CAN'T *MAINTAIN* CONTROL OVER WHATEVER IT HAS INFECTED.

AND THEN THE INFECTED TARGET BEGINS TO BREAK DOWN. TO DEVOLVE —

THE VIROID CAN ONLY SURVIVE BY FINDING ITS *NEXT* TARGET TO INFECT AND TAKE OVER.

BUT I NEVER SAW ANY *CHANGE* IN O'BRIEN! NOT LIKE THIS!

HE WAS INFECTED FOR ONLY A BRIEF PERIOD. HARDLY MORE THAN A CARRIER OF THE VIROID, INTO THE STATION ITSELF.

YOU INFECTED O'BRIEN — DIDN'T YOU? AS PART OF YOUR *RESEARCH*!

LET'S JUST SAY THAT YOUR FRIEND WAS A CONVENIENT *INSTRUMENT* —

FOR EXPANDING SCIENTIFIC *KNOWLEDGE*.

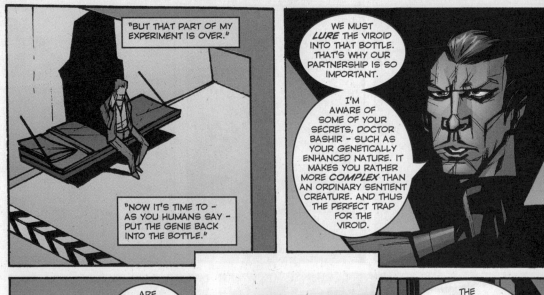

"BUT THAT PART OF MY EXPERIMENT IS OVER."

"NOW IT'S TIME TO - AS YOU HUMANS SAY - PUT THE GENIE BACK INTO THE BOTTLE."

WE MUST *LURE* THE VIROID INTO THAT BOTTLE. THAT'S WHY OUR PARTNERSHIP IS SO IMPORTANT.

I'M AWARE OF SOME OF YOUR SECRETS, DOCTOR BASHIR - SUCH AS YOUR GENETICALLY ENHANCED NATURE. IT MAKES YOU RATHER MORE *COMPLEX* THAN AN ORDINARY SENTIENT CREATURE. AND THUS THE PERFECT TRAP FOR THE VIROID.

ARE YOU SAYING THAT I SHOULD LET MYSELF BE INFECTED BY THIS... *VIROID?*

IT ALL DEPENDS, DOCTOR -

"DO YOU WANT TO SAVE YOUR FRIEND - OR NOT?"

THE SO-CALLED SABOTAGE IS NOTHING BUT A TEMPORARY DEFORMATION OF DS9'S PHYSICAL STRUCTURE. REMOVE THE VIROID, AND THE DAMAGE WILL DISAPPEAR -

AND THEN THERE'S NO EVIDENCE AGAINST O'BRIEN. AND YOUR FRIEND IS A FREE MAN AGAIN.

BUT THEN *I'D* BE INFECTED WITH THE VIROID - CORRECT?

ONLY TEMPORARILY, DOCTOR -

ROMULAN MILITARY TECHNOLOGY - WE CALL IT "THERAPEUTIC DEATH."

THE SERUM IS INERT AND HARMLESS UNTIL IT IS TRIGGERED BY REMOTE CONTROL. THEN IT CREATES A DEATH-LIKE COMA - SO THAT A WOUNDED SOLDIER CAN BE REMOVED FROM THE BATTLEFIELD AND REVIVED LATER, FOR APPROPRIATE MEDICAL ATTENTION.

BUT IF WE FIRST LURE THE VIROID INTO YOU, AND THEN TRIGGER SUCH A THERA-PUTIC DEATH COMA –

THEN THE ONLY WAY THE VIROID WILL BE ABLE TO SURVIVE IS FOR IT TO EXIT YOUR SYSTEM AND INTO THE INERT SAFEKEEPING CONTAINER THAT I'VE PREPARED FOR IT.

AND THEN THE GENIE IS BACK INSIDE THE BOTTLE.

DO WE HAVE A DEAL, DOCTOR?

I DON'T FEEL ANYTHING.

YOU WON'T – UNTIL I TRIGGER THE SERUM.

NOW IT'S TIME FOR THE REST OF OUR... PROCEDURE.

THIS AREA IS HIGHLY INFECTED WITH THE VIROID. IT'S PERFECT FOR US.

WHAT IS IT? WHAT'S WRONG?

THERE'S NOTHING WRONG...

NOTHING AT ALL.

WAIT A MINUTE –

SOMETHING'S GONE WRONG –

IT'S NOT WORKING!

I TRIGGERED THE SERUM! YOU SHOULD HAVE GONE INTO A COMA – *INSTANTLY!*

THAT'S RIGHT. THAT'S WHAT *SHOULD* HAVE HAPPENED –

IF I HAD ACTUALLY INJECTED THE SERUM.

BUT... DOCTOR BASHIR...

YOU'RE NOT TALKING TO BASHIR NOW.

YOU'RE TALKING TO THE VIROID.

WHAT YOU DIDN'T REALIZE IS THAT BASHIR WAS *ALREADY* INFECTED WITH THE VIROID –

INFECTED...

"AND WITH PLANS."

"BIG PLANS."

PRESENTS

Paramount COMICS®

K. W. JETER — WRITER
TOBY CYPRESS — PENCILS
JASON MARTIN & MARK IRWIN — INKS
BAD@$$ — COLORS
NAGHMEH ZAND — LETTERS
JEFF MARIOTTE — EDITS

STAR TREK: DEEP SPACE NINE®
N - VECTOR
CHAPTER 3

BASED ON STAR TREK: DEEP SPACE NINE®

THAT'S INCREDIBLE...

THE REACTOR... IT'S IN PERFECT CONDITION! READY TO GO ON-LINE AGAIN...

HOW DID YOUR CREW GET IT REPAIRED SO FAST?

WE DIDN'T.

WHAT'RE YOU TALKING ABOUT?

IT FIXED ITSELF.

IS THIS SOME KIND OF A JOKE?

I WOULDN'T JOKE ABOUT SOMETHING LIKE THIS, COLONEL. IT'S TRUE—

I'VE PERSONALLY INSPECTED EVERY SITE ON BOARD THE STATION, WHERE THERE APPEARED TO HAVE BEEN DELIBERATE SABOTAGE. AND NOW THERE'S NO SIGN OF ANY DAMAGE AT ALL!

THE EVIDENCE IS GONE—

THERE IS NO SABOTAGE!

SO WHAT YOU'RE TELLING ME, LIEUTENANT, IS THAT ALL THE DAMAGE THAT WAS MYSTERIOUSLY DONE TO THE STATION'S EQUIPMENT – DAMAGE THAT RESULTED IN ONE OF THE REACTOR CHAMBERS EXPLODING AND KILLING A CREW-MEMBER – NOW ALL THAT APPARENT SABOTAGE HAS SUDDENLY DISAPPEARED.

JUST AS IF THE STATION'S EQUIPMENT SOMEHOW *HEALED* ITSELF.

IT SEEMS TO BE WHAT HAPPENED.

LIEUTENANT...

DAMAGED EQUIPMENT DOESN'T JUST HEAL ITSELF—

WHAT'S GOING ON?

THAT'S A GOOD QUESTION.

AND ONE FOR WHICH I HOPED *YOU* WOULD HAVE THE ANSWER, COLONEL KIRA.

I CAN CONFIRM YOUR ACTING SECURITY CHIEF'S REPORT ABOUT THE SO-CALLED SABOTAGE ABOARD DS9.

I'VE DONE MY OWN INVESTIGATION INTO THIS MATTER. LT. NOG IS ABSOLUTELY CORRECT: THERE'S NO LONGER ANY SIGN OF DELIBERATE DAMAGE TO THE STATION'S EQUIPMENT—

YOU HAD NO AUTHORITY TO DO THAT! THE DEFIANT IS YOUR COMMAND, NOT DS9—

MY AUTHORIZATION COMES DIRECTLY FROM STARFLEET. QUESTIONS HAVE ALREADY BEEN RAISED, COLONEL, REGARDING THE MANNER IN WHICH YOU'RE RUNNING THIS STATION.

THERE WILL BE EVEN MORE QUESTIONS NOW.

IT'S NOT ENOUGH THAT THE EVIDENCE OF SABOTAGE HAS DISAPPEARED.

UNTIL YOU CAN TELL STARFLEET COMMAND EXACTLY WHAT HAPPENED HERE - AND THAT IT WON'T HAPPEN AGAIN - THEN *YOU'RE* THE ONE WHO'S UNDER SUSPICION.

I SUGGEST, COLONEL, THAT YOU GET TO THE BOTTOM OF THIS - *IMMEDIATELY.*

"AHH... PEACE AND QUIET AT LAST..."

"FAR FROM ALL THOSE PETTY SQUABBLES..."

ALL THAT STUFF THAT GETS IN THE WAY OF AN HONEST BUSINESSMAN.

OR A DISHONEST ONE, FOR THAT MATTER.

OF COURSE, I DON'T MEAN TO *PRY*, VIQTOR, BUT SINCE WE'RE PARTNERS AND ALL—

PERHAPS YOU COULD TELL ME EXACTLY WHERE WE'RE HEADED?

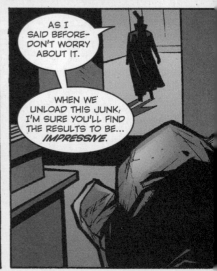

AS I SAID BEFORE— DON'T WORRY ABOUT IT.

WHEN WE UNLOAD THIS JUNK, I'M SURE YOU'LL FIND THE RESULTS TO BE... *IMPRESSIVE.*

SLAM!

MILES...

YOU'RE A FREE MAN.

SHORTLY...

THERE'S *NO EVIDENCE* AGAINST ME? WHAT HAPPENED TO IT?

PERHAPS IT NEVER EXISTED...

BUT IT REALLY DOESN'T MATTER NOW, DOES IT? THE CHARGES OF SABOTAGE HAVE BEEN DROPPED AND YOUR RECORD COMPLETELY CLEARED.

GIVE MY BEST WISHES TO YOUR WIFE KEIKO WHEN YOU REACH HOME.

DOESN'T REALLY SEEM LIKE HIM, DOES IT?

THAT'S BECAUSE IT'S *NOT* HIM.

LOOK, I KNOW WHAT I'M TALKING ABOUT. JULIAN WAS MY BEST FRIEND WHILE I WAS STATIONED HERE AT DS9 – I'VE SPENT A LOT OF TIME WITH JULIAN –

AND THIS JULIAN ISN'T HIM.

MILES IS RIGHT –

WHOEVER – OR *WHATEVER* – IT IS, IT'S NOT THE JULIAN BASHIR THAT I KNOW, EITHER.

THERE'S SOMETHING *DIFFERENT* ABOUT HIM NOW. SOMETHING COLDER, MORE REMOTE – AND *EVIL*.

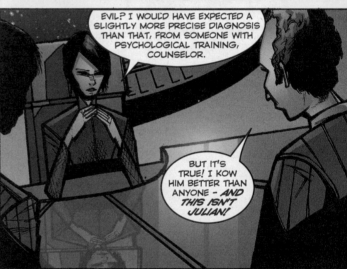

EVIL? I WOULD HAVE EXPECTED A SLIGHTLY MORE PRECISE DIAGNOSIS THAN THAT, FROM SOMEONE WITH PSYCHOLOGICAL TRAINING, COUNSELOR.

BUT IT'S TRUE! I KOW HIM BETTER THAN ANYONE – *AND THIS ISN'T JULIAN!*

HAVE YOU CONSIDERED THE POSSIBILITY...

THAT THE PROBLEM ISN'T WITH JULIAN – BUT WITH YOU?

EVERYONE ABOARD THE STATION HAS BEEN UNDER A *LOT* OF STRESS. WOULDN'T YOU AGREE, EZRI?

YES, BUT–

THIS WHOLE SABOTAGE BUSINESS, AND THE ACCUSATIONS AGAINST OUR FORMER OPS CHIEF – IT'S PUT EVERYBODY ON EDGE. INCLUDING JULIAN.

BUT RIGHT NOW, I'M JUST GLAD IT'S *OVER*.

AND I'M *NOT* GOING TO START IT UP AGAIN.

"STARFLEET – AND OUR COMMANDER JAST IN PARTICULAR – IS NOT EXACTLY PLEASED WITH EVIDENCE OF SABOTAGE JUST APPEARING AND THEN DISAPPEARING."

"THERE'S A CLOSE WATCH BEING KEPT ON THIS STATION. WE CAN'T AFFORD ANOTHER MESS LIKE THIS LAST ONE."

IT WAS GOOD SEEING YOU AGAIN, MILES – EVEN UNDER THESE CIRCUMSTANCES.

HAVE A GOOD TRIP BACK TO THE ACADEMY. AND GIVE MY LOVE TO KEIKO, MOLLY, AND YOSHI.

NOW WHAT DO WE DO?

PERHAPS I MIGHT BE ABLE TO HELP YOU.

YOU'RE CORRECT ABOUT YOUR FRIEND. THAT'S NOT JULIAN BASHIR YOU'RE DEALING WITH...

OR AT LEAST, NOT *ENTIRELY*.

AND JUST HOW WOULD YOU KNOW THAT?

LET'S JUST SAY... THAT I'M THE ONE WITH THE ANSWERS.

THE ANSWERS YOU NEED.

THAT IS, OF COURSE, IF YOU WANT TO SAVE YOUR FRIEND.

SHORTLY...

... IF NOTHING ELSE, THE RESULTS HAVE BEEN INTERESTING.

TO SAY THE LEAST.

LET ME SEE IF I'VE GOT THIS STRAIGHT—

YOU'VE LEFT JULIAN INFECTED WITH THIS... THIS *VIROID*—

AND YOU FIND THAT *INTERESTING*?

DON'T YOU? BUT OF COURSE, THE PROBLEM IS...

WHAT DO WE DO ABOUT IT NOW?

"SO WHAT I WANT TO KNOW IS..."

"WHAT DO WE DO NOW?"

I MEAN... THIS IS A TOTALLY EMPTY SECTOR OF THE ALPHA QUADRANT! WHERE ARE THE CUSTOMERS OUT HERE?

YOU TOLD ME THAT WE'D MAKE A FORTUNE UNLOADING THE OLD JUNK WE TOOK OUT OF THE DS9 STORAGE LOCKERS...

WE CAN'T *MAKE* MONEY IF THERE ISN'T ANYONE WHOSE MONEY WE CAN *TAKE!*

IS THAT ANOTHER ONE OF THOSE FERENGI RULES OF ACQUISITION THAT YOU KEEP TELLING ME ABOUT?

NO, IT'S JUST COMMON SENSE! I'VE NEVER GONE INTO BUSINESS WITH ANYONE SO IDIOTIC THAT HE DIDN'T UNDERSTAND THAT MUCH!

NOT, OF COURSE, THAT YOU'RE AN IDIOT OR ANYTHING... I DIDN'T *MEAN* THAT...

BUT PERHAPS BUSINESS ISN'T A *SPECIALTY* OF YOURS... THE WAY IT IS FOR A FERENGI...

YOU'VE DUMPED OUT OUR CARGO! EVERYTHING WE BROUGHT HERE FROM DS9!

"DON'T WORRY..."

"EVERYTHING'S GOING ACCORDING TO PLAN."

WHAT PLAN?

SO *THIS* WAS THE PLAN!

THERE ISN'T TIME TO CONVINCE COLONEL KIRA – OR ANYBODY IN STARFLEET – TO HELP US. THE VIROID HAS ALREADY SET ITS PLANS INTO MOTION.

IF WE CAN'T STOP IT NOW – AND IMMEDIATELY – THEN I CAN ASSURE YOU...

THERE WILL BE WORSE – MUCH WORSE – TO COME.

SO WE HAVE TO FIND SOME WAY OF GETTING THE VIROID *OUT* OF JULIAN–

PRECISELY – AND INTO THE INERT CONTAINER THAT I'VE ALREADY PREPARED FOR IT.

AND WITHOUT HARMING JULIAN.

THAT MAKES IT A LITTLE MORE DIFFICULT. BUT–

I DIDN'T THINK I COULD GET HIS FRIENDS' ASSISTANCE, OTHERWISE.

THIS ROMULAN 'THERAPEUTIC DEATH' SERUM YOU TOLD US ABOUT – THAT WOULD DO THE JOB.

IF WE HAD A PLAN FOR GETTING IT INTO JULIAN'S SYSTEM.

BUT I *DO* HAVE A PLAN.

I *ALWAYS* HAVE ONE.

YOU REALIZE, OF COURSE, THAT I'M *ALREADY* DISOBEYING ORDERS, BY NOT HEADING BACK TO THE ACADEMY.

THERE'S NO TIME TO WORRY ABOUT THAT NOW—

MY DIPLOMATIC PASS GOT US HERE ABOARD THE *DEFIANT*. BUT NO ONE IS EXPECTING YOU TO SHOW UP AT THE RECEPTION FOR THE ROMULAN AMBASSADOR.

SO YOU'RE FREE TO TAKE CARE OF YOUR PART OF OUR PLAN — AND I'LL TAKE CARE OF MINE.

THIS IS THE STUPIDEST THING I'VE EVER DONE...

I JUST GOT CLEARED OF SABOTAGE CHARGES — AND NOW I'M GOING TO COMMIT IT!

WELL... HERE GOES...

... AND OF COURSE, THE FEDERATION WOULD WANT TO CO-OPERATE WITH ITS NEW ALLIES ON ALL AREAS OF MEDICAL RESEARCH.

AND I'M SURE YOU WOULD BE HAPPY TO HELP THEM, WOULDN'T YOU, DOCTOR BASHIR?

COMMANDER JAST, WHAT IS THIS PERSON DOING HERE? HE IS NOT ENTIRELY A WELCOME FIGURE WITHIN THE ROMULAN COUNCIL.

THAT MAY BE. BUT YOU MIGHT NOT BE SO EAGER TO ACCEPT DOCTOR BASHIR'S OFFERS OF ASSISTANCE...

IF YOU KNEW AS MUCH ABOUT HIM AS *I* DO.

YOUR ATTEMPT TO INTERFERE IS FUTILE —

ALL PERSONNEL ALERT! ALL PERSONNEL ALERT —

WHAT'S THAT?

SECURITY BREACH - SOMETHING'S HAPPENING WITH THE SHIP'S CENTRAL POWER SYSTEM -

HOW INTERESTING. AND WHAT A COINCIDENCE -

THE EXACT SAME KIND OF 'SABOTAGE' THAT HAPPENED ABOARD DS9 -

UNLESS, OF COURSE, IT'S *NOT* A COINCIDENCE.

OVERLOAD CONDITIONS IN THE MAIN REACTION CHAMBER, SIR. THERE APPEARS TO HAVE BEEN A MANUAL BYPASS OF THE MONITORING CONTROLS -

WHICH IS *EXACTLY* WHAT HAPPENED ON DS9, ISN'T IT? WHICH MEANS -

YOU *HAVEN'T* COVERED UP YOUR TRAIL AS WELL AS YOU THOUGHT YOU DID, HAVE YOU?

JUST WHAT ARE YOU TALKING ABOUT?

IT'S NOT IMPORTANT THAT YOU KNOW THAT, COMMANDER -

AS LONG AS *IT* DOES.

HE'D BETTER SHOW UP SOON.

OR THIS WHOLE SHIP IS GOING TO BLOW!

O'BRIEN —

YOU SHOULD HAVE LEFT WHEN YOU HAD THE CHANCE. BECAUSE NOW —

YOU DON'T HAVE ANY MORE CHANCES!

IT APPEARS THAT YOU WERE CORRECT, DOCTOR SENAY.

PROCEED.

PHFFT

IF ANYTHING HAPPENS TO HIM... I PROMISE YOU...

YOU'LL BE THE ONE WHO'S DEAD.

WHERE... AM I...

JUST KEEP STILL. YOU'LL BE FINE NOW...

WHAT HAPPENED?

SENAY GAVE YOU THE ANTIDOTE TO THE 'THERAPEUTIC DEATH' SERUM —

AFTER HE GOT THE VIROID OUT OF YOU AND SAFELY BOTTLED UP.

THEN IT'S ALL OVER.

NO —

"IT'S STILL OUT THERE."

"WE'VE HAD A NARROW ESCAPE..."

Paramount COMICS®

STAR TREK: DEEP SPACE NINE®
N - VECTOR
CHAPTER 4
BASED ON STAR TREK: DEEP SPACE NINE®

PRESENTS

K. W. JETER — WRITER
TOBY CYPRESS — PENCILS
JASON MARTIN — INKS
BAD@$$ — COLORS
NAGHMEH ZAND — LETTERS
JEFF MARIOTTE — EDITS

AND IT'S NO THANKS TO *ME*.

IT'S NOTHING TO *BLAME* YOURSELF FOR--

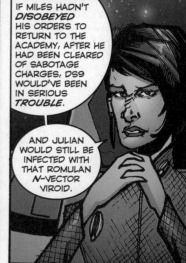

IF MILES HADN'T *DISOBEYED* HIS ORDERS TO RETURN TO THE ACADEMY, AFTER HE HAD BEEN CLEARED OF SABOTAGE CHARGES, DS9 WOULD'VE BEEN IN SERIOUS *TROUBLE*.

AND JULIAN WOULD STILL BE INFECTED WITH THAT ROMULAN *N*-VECTOR VIROID.

BUT YOU'VE DONE *ENOUGH*-- YOU'RE GOING HOME TO KEIKO AND YOUR KIDS.

AND THAT'S *ONE* ORDER YOU'RE *NOT* DISOBEYING.

BUT--

WE CAN TAKE CARE OF IT FROM HERE. AND WE WILL.

YOU'RE NOT TAKING CARE OF *ANYTHING*--

NOT WITHOUT *ME*.

YOU'VE BEEN ABLE TO CONVINCE COMMANDER JAST THAT THE CRISIS IS *OVER*--BUT YOU *KNOW* THAT IT'S NOT.

AND *I'M* THE ONLY ONE WHO CAN HALT THE SPREAD OF THE *N*-VECTOR VIROID.

HAVEN'T YOU DONE ENOUGH ALREADY, SENAY? YOU BROUGHT THE VIROID HERE TO DS9, YOU INFECTED THE STATION *AND* OUR MEDICAL CHIEF WITH IT--

I'M NOT SURE IF WE COULD *STAND* ANY MORE HELP FROM YOU.

YOUR CREW AND YOUR FORMER OPS CHIEF WERE USEFUL TO ME, IN GETTING THE VIROID FRAGMENT SAFELY BOTTLED UP AGAIN.

BUT THE VIROID *ITSELF*-- THE MAIN *ENTITY*-- HAS SUCCEEDED IN *ESCAPING* FROM DS9.

"*I'M* THE ONLY ONE WHO KNOWS WHERE IT'S *GONE*..."

"AND WHAT ITS *PLANS* ARE."

"NOW I UNDERSTAND..."

THIS IS WHAT THE PLAN WAS! WE'LL MAKE A FORTUNE, SELLING OFF SOMETHING LIKE THIS!

OF COURSE, IT'S NOT QUITE PRIME REAL ESTATE...

BUT WE STILL SHOULD BE ABLE TO TURN A SUBSTANTIAL PROFIT FROM IT, VIQTOR.

VIQTOR?

WHERE ARE YOU?

WE NEED TO MAKE OUR MARKETING PLANS...

VIQTOR... THIS IS NO TIME TO PLAY HIDE-AND-SEEK...

THERE'S BUSINESS TO TAKE CARE OF...

VIQTOR...

WHAT A TIME FOR A PARTNER TO GO *DISAPPEARING*...

FROM NOW ON, I'M ONLY GOING INTO BUSINESS WITH *NORMAL* CROOKS AND SWINDLERS.

VIQTOR?

I'M BEGINNING...

TO NOT *LIKE* THIS BUSINESS AT ALL...

"SINCE I'M THE ONLY ONE WHO KNOWS HOW TO DEAL WITH THE VIROID..."

THEN I SHOULD HAVE COMPLETE AUTHORITY OVER ANY EXPEDITION GOING AFTER IT. THAT'S NOT A REQUEST.

IT'S A DEMAND. AND NON-NEGOTIABLE.

AND WHY SHOULD WE GO AFTER IT AT ALL? I'M FREE OF THE VIROID-- AND DS9 HAS BEEN *DISINFECTED* FROM IT, AS WELL.

SO TELL US, DOCTOR SENAY--*WHAT IS IT THAT MAKES THIS VIROID SO DANGEROUS?*

YOU DON'T NEED TO *KNOW* THAT.

BUT YOU NEED TO TELL US-- OR YOU CAN TRY TO HUNT IT DOWN, *WITHOUT* ANY HELP FROM US.

VERY WELL. BUT IF YOU DON'T LIKE WHAT YOU HEAR-- IT'S NOT MY FAULT.

"THE *N*-VECTOR VIROID WAS POWERFUL WHEN I DISCOVERED IT--BUT IT HAS EVEN *MORE* POWERS NOW."

"POWERS THAT I *GAVE* IT."

"I CREATED A *MORPHETIC SUBSTRATE* FOR THE VIROID--A BASIC PROTOPLASMIC SUBSTANCE THAT THE VIROID CAN SHAPE INTO ANY FORM, LIVING OR MECHANICAL, ON ITS OWN OR BY INCORPORATING OTHER MATTER THAT IS HAS INFECTED."

"THE MILITARY APPLICATIONS OF SUCH AS CREATION ARE, OF COURSE, OBVIOUS."

"THE ALTERED VIROID IS NOT A TRUE SHAPE-SHIFTER, SUCH AS YOUR FORMER SECURITY CHIEF ODO. A SEGMENT OF IT CAN ONLY SET INTO *ONE* SHAPE, WHICH THEN SLOWLY BEGINS TO DEVOLVE; ITS ESSENCE MUST THEN BE REABSORBED INTO THE LARGER *N*-VECTOR VIROID."

I HAD NOT YET FOUND A WAY TO STABILIZE THE VIROID'S ASSUMED SHAPES, WHEN MY RESEARCH WAS INTERRUPTED BY THE ROMULAN AUTHORITIES.

FINALLY, I WAS ALLOWED TO RETURN--ONLY TO FIND THAT THE VIROID HAD INFECTED THE STATION DURING MY ABSENCE. TRUE, THE STATION HAS NOW BEEN CLEANSED, BUT THE VIROID HAS ESCAPED, TAKING THE MORPHETIC SUBSTRATE AND A LARGE QUANTITY OF INFECTED SCRAP MATERIAL WITH IT.

IT WILL USE THOSE THINGS TO CREATE AN IMMENSE *SPORULATING BODY*--

"A MASSIVE CONSTRUCT OF VIROID-INFECTED MATERIAL--"

"AND *THAT* IS WHERE THE DANGER LIES."

"WHEN IT BREAKS APART, *EVERY* PIECE WILL CONTAIN THE *N*-VECTOR VIROID--"

"SPREADING THE VIROID THROUGHOUT THE *GALAXY,* INFECTING EVERYTHING WITH WHICH IT COMES INTO *CONTACT*--"

"*EVERYTHING.*"

AND YOU *CREATED* THIS THING.

AND I CAN CONTROL IT--

BUT ONLY IF I'M IN *COMMAND.*

THERE ISN'T TIME TO *ARGUE.* WE'LL HAVE TO DO AS HE SAYS.

VERY WELL--

BUT IF YOU DON'T SUCCEED--YOU WON'T HAVE TO WORRY ABOUT THE VIROID ANY LONGER.

OR ANYTHING *ELSE.* DO YOU UNDERSTAND?

ALL I NEED TO DO IS GET BACK ABOARD THE TRANSPORT SHIP THAT BROUGHT ME HERE, AND I'LL HEAD STRAIGHT FOR THE *REAL* DS9.

THIS REAL ESTATE ISN'T SO VALUABLE THAT IT'S WORTH *THIS* MUCH TROUBLE.

FRANKLY, I DON'T KNOW IF I *COULD* UNLOAD THIS PLACE OFF ON ANYBODY!

LET ME SEE IF I CAN FIND THE TRANSPORT SHIP...

WELL...

"I GUESS I'M NOT GETTING BACK TO DS9 ABOARD *THAT*."

YOU'RE SURE ABOUT THIS?

ABSOLUTELY-- WHILE THE STATION WAS STILL INFECTED WITH THE VIROID, NOG SET UP SECURITY SCANNERS AT ALL THE DOCKS.

THE VIROID ESCAPED THE STATION, ALL RIGHT--WITH QUARK!

IS THAT TRUE? IT'S YOUR UNCLE THAT LEFT THE STATION WITH THE VIROID?

YES, SIR--HE MUST HAVE THOUGHT HE HAD SOME KIND OF "BUSINESS ARRANGEMENT" WITH THE VIROID'S HUMANOID FORM.

TYPICAL.

YOU'RE GOING ALONG WITH BASHIR AND SENAY.

AND MAKE SURE YOU BRING QUARK BACK IN ONE PIECE--

SO I CAN TAKE HIM APART!

WHAT HAPPENS IF QUARK AND THE VIROID AREN'T AT THE COORDINATES YOU'VE GIVEN US?

DON'T WORRY ABOUT THAT. I KNOW THE VIROID BETTER THAN--

I'VE PICKED UP A *SIGNAL!*

...ANYBODY OUT THERE? I COULD USE *HELP* RIGHT ABOUT NOW...

THAT'S QUARK!

LET ME SPEAK TO HIM.

LISTEN TO ME VERY CAREFULLY. YOU ARE IN GREAT DANGER--

EXCUSE ME, BUT I ALREADY KNOW THAT.

BUT IT IS NOT AS BAD AS IT MIGHT SEEM...

YOU'VE ALREADY BEEN INFECTED ONCE BY THE N-VECTOR VIROID--SO YOU HAVE IMMUNITY FROM IT NOW.

IT CAN'T INFECT YOU AGAIN OR ABSORB YOU INTO ITSELF--

VIROID? INFECTED? WHAT ARE YOU *TALKING* ABOUT?

IT WILL ALL BE EXPLAINED LATER. BUT RIGHT NOW, YOU MUST...BZZZT... GRAKK...FZFZZZ...

WHAT? WHAT WAS THAT? HELLO...

THE SIGNAL HAS BEEN CUT OFF--

THAT WASN'T TOO SMART OF YOU, DOCTOR SENAY. YOU'VE JUST MANAGED TO *WARN* THE VIROID THAT QUARK IS IMMUNE TO ITS CONTROL.

IT'S NOT GOING TO *WAIT* UNTIL WE GET THERE TO HELP QUARK--IT'LL TRY TO ELIMINATE HIM *RIGHT NOW.*

I'M *IMMUNE* FROM SOMETHING? I DON'T GET IT.

WHAT'S THAT SUPPOSED TO--

HEY!

I DON'T LIKE THIS...

AND I *REALLY* DON'T LIKE THAT.

SCRREEEEEEEE rrrrrr

SCRREEEEEEE.....

CRAKKK_AKKK_AKK....

CRREEEEEEOR....

THIS PLACE SOUNDS LIKE IT'S COMING *APART!*

PRIME REAL ESTATE, INDEED...

I WOULDN'T BE ABLE TO UNLOAD *THIS* DUMP ON EVEN A *KLINGON*...

JUST LOOK AT THIS PLACE!

THEY WERE EXPECTING *CUSTOMERS*...?

I ALWAYS KNEW THESE WOULD BE USEFUL FOR SOMETHING OTHER THAN PROVIDING ROMANTIC ATMOSPHERE.

NOW TO GET THIS PLACE UP AND RUNNING AGAIN...

I'VE GOT A FIX ON THE SOURCE OF QUARK'S DISTRESS SIGNAL--

IT CAME RIGHT FROM THE COORDINATES THAT SENAY ALREADY GAVE US.

AS I SAID...

I KNOW THE VIROID AND ITS PLANS BETTER THAN *ANYONE*.

OBVIOUSLY, IF THIS PLACE ISN'T WORKING...

IT NEEDS TO BE *FIXED*.

HOW HARD CAN IT BE?

HUMANS AND KLINGONS FIX THESE KINDS OF THINGS ALL THE TIME.

KRRRKRRRAAK...

SCRRREEEEEEEE...

OH OH.

MAYBE I CAN PUT IT BACK THE WAY IT WAS...

PERHAPS *WE* CAN HELP YOU.

WHO... WHO ARE *YOU*...

LIKE I SAID...WE'RE HERE TO *HELP* YOU.

THAT'S ALL RIGHT-- REALLY--

YOU DON'T NEED TO TROUBLE YOURSELVES--I'LL BE FINE...

THERE'S NO PLACE TO *DOCK!*

I DON'T CARE--I'M TAKING US IN.

IS IT TOO LATE TO MAKE A *DEAL* HERE? WHAT EXACTLY IS IT THAT YOU PEOPLE *WANT?*

WE HAVE OUR *OWN* PLANS.

AND *NOTHING'S* GOING TO--

WE DON'T HAVE MUCH TIME--

BEFORE THE VIROID ABSORBS *THIS* SHIP AS WELL. LET'S GO!

THIS WAY!

I DON'T THINK I NEED TO STICK AROUND--

UNCLE *QUARK!*

QUARK-- IT'S US--

OH... THE *REAL* ONES...

GET HIM BACK TO THE RUNABOUT-- *IMMEDIATELY!*

YOU WON'T *BELIEVE* THE CONDITION THIS PLACE IS IN...

NOW WHAT ARE WE GOING TO DO ABOUT THE VIROID?

NOTHING.

NOTHING? WHAT ARE YOU *TALKING* ABOUT?

IT'S *SIMPLE*...

WE'VE FORCED THE VIROID'S HAND. IT'S NOT *READY* TO BREAK APART INTO SPORES-- IT NEEDED MORE *TIME* TO REACH THAT POINT.

NOW THAT ITS LOCATION HAS BEEN *DISCOVERED*, IT MUST *DEFEND* ITSELF, THE ONLY WAY IT KNOWS HOW. IT MUST GO *DORMANT!*

BUT WHAT IF YOU'RE *WRONG* ABOUT THAT?

I'M NOT WRONG... I'M BETTING MY *LIFE* ON IT.

GET BACK TO THE RUNABOUT. *I'M* STAYING HERE.

THE *N*-VECTOR VIROID WAS SENAY'S DISCOVERY AND HIS CREATION-- WHEN IT *IMPLODED* OUT OF *EXISTENCE*, HE PREFERRED TO GO *WITH* IT.

BUT THE VIROID'S NOT REALLY *GONE*, IS IT? LIKE A BLACK HOLE OR SOME OTHER KIND OF SPACE ANOMALY--IT COULD SHOW UP *ANYWHERE!*

TRUE...

I DON'T CARE IF IT SHOWS UP AGAIN OR NOT--

AS LONG AS IT'S SOMEONE *ELSE'S* PROBLEM WHEN IT DOES!

WHEN THE VIROID *FIRST* SHOWED UP, AT LEAST I HAD A DEBT *COLLECTOR*--

OH, *SURE*; SOMEONE ELSE'S PROBLEM!

NOW ALL I'VE GOT ARE THE *DEBTS!*

THE END.

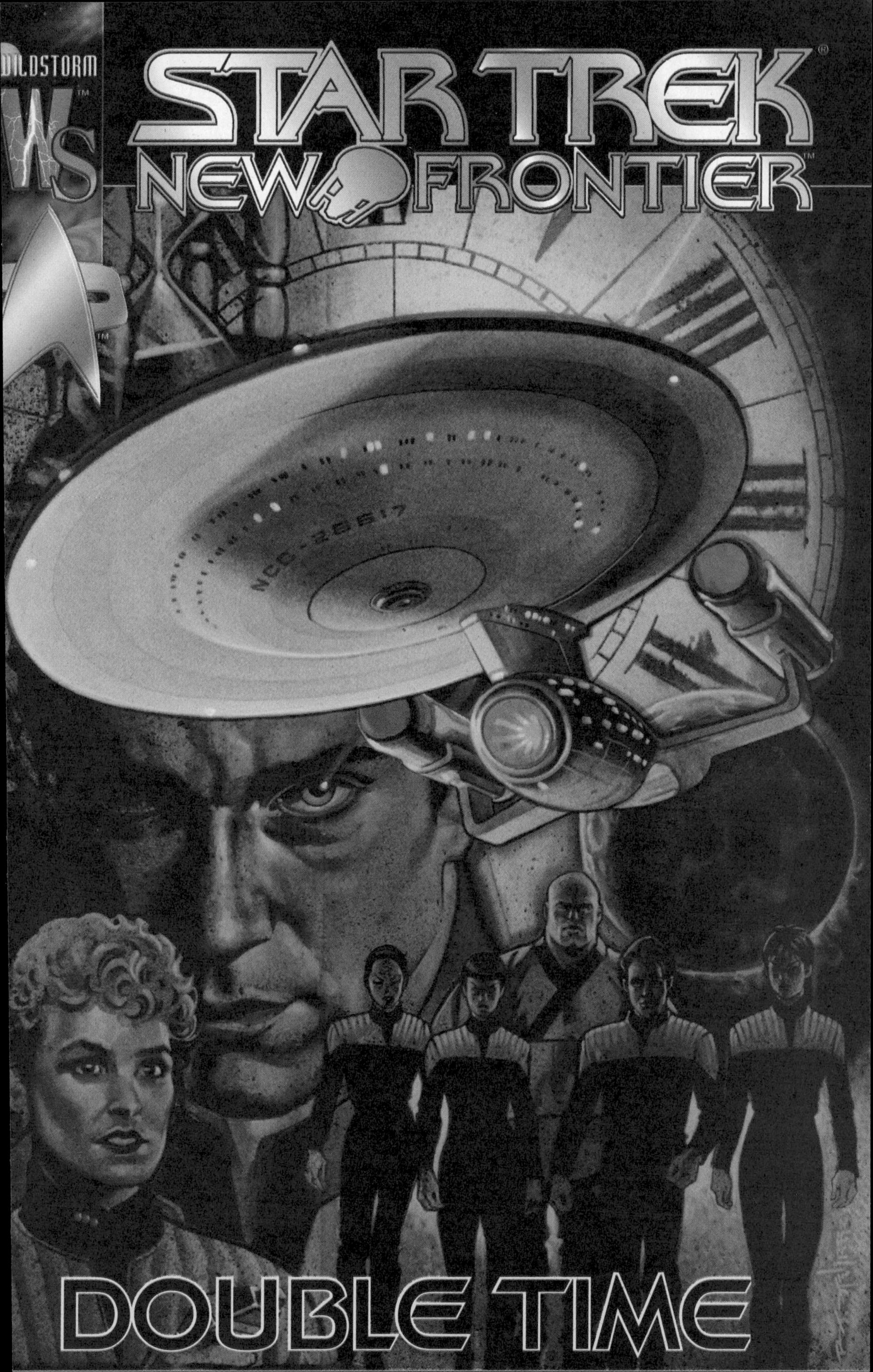
WILDSTORM
WS
STAR TREK
NEW FRONTIER
NCC-2893
DOUBLE TIME

NOW...

CAPTAIN MACKENZIE CALHOUN HAD NEVER BELIEVED IN THE CONCEPT OF A SILENCE SO COMPLETE THAT ONE COULD HEAR THE BEATING OF ONE'S OWN *HEART*.

BUT AS THE THUMPING AGAINST HIS CHEST BECOMES MORE AUDIBLE WITH EVERY MOMENT, HE IS REMINDED THAT PART OF THE REASON SOME THINGS BECOME CLICHÉS...

...IS BECAUSE THEY ARE *TRUE*.

AND EACH BEAT OF HIS HEART SYMBOLIZES A MOMENT, A SECOND, ONE SPILLING INTO ANOTHER. TIME SLIPPING AWAY LIKE AN UNASSAILABLE UNDERTOW...

...PULLING AWAY WITH IT THE LIFE OF A WORLD.

OTHER NOISES BEGIN TO DRIFT TOWARD HIM NOW. MEMBERS OF HIS CREW, GATHERING DATA, PREPARING WHAT WILL BE THE FINAL REPORT ON THE UNHAPPY END OF THE WORLD ONCE KNOWN AS HARESH.

A WORLD ONCE THRIVING, PROSPEROUS, FILLED WITH POTENTIAL... UNTIL THE ARRIVAL OF A RACE CALHOUN HAS CROSSED SWORDS WITH BEFORE.

AND, AT WORST... LETHAL.

THE REDEEMERS. ZEALOTS WHO SPREAD THE WORD OF THEIR BELOVED GOD, XANT. AND THOSE WHO ARE NOT WILLING TO ACCEPT THAT WORD CAN FIND THEMSELVES IN STRAITS THAT, AT BEST, COULD BE CALLED DIRE.

IT IS THE LATTER THAT HAS OCCURRED THIS DAY. AND CALHOUN... UNABLE TO PREVENT IT... SEEKS AN OUTLET FOR HIS FRUSTRATION.

I DON'T SEE THAT THAT'S GOING TO *HELP*, CAPTAIN. SMASHING IN THE SKULL OF A DEAD MAN WITH A ROCK.

THIS DEAD MAN TOOK AN ENTIRE *RACE* WITH HIM, COMMANDER.

I KNOW HE DID, MAC. AND BELIEVE ME, IF I THOUGHT DECAPITATING A CORPSE WOULD BRING THEM BACK TO LIFE, I'D BE THE FIRST IN LINE WITH A BOULDER.

LOOK, DO IT IF IT'LL MAKE YOU *FEEL* BETTER.

≥SIGH≤

VERY WISE, CAPTAIN. IT HAS LESS TO DO WITH *WISDOM* THAN IT DOES WITH THE FACT THAT YOU TOOK ALL THE *FUN* OUT OF IT.

CAPTAIN... I'VE FINISHED MY ANALYSIS OF THE SITUATION. AS WE SUSPECTED, THE INTERNAL, LETHAL VIRUS WHICH CERTAIN REDEEMERS CARRY WITHIN THEIR BLOODSTREAM--WHICH SERVES AS A RETALIATORY "FINAL SOLUTION" IN THE EVENT OF *HARM* TO A REDEEMER'S PERSON-- WAS RESPONSIBLE FOR THIS.

IMPRESSIVE THAT IT DISSIPATES AS QUICKLY AS IT DOES. I'VE TAKEN SOME BLOOD SAMPLES THAT--

SOLETA *LATER.* RIGHT?

I SUPPO NOT

YES, CAPTAIN. WHATEVER YOU SAY.

CAPTAIN... I KNOW YOU AS WELL AS ANYBODY *CAN.* YEARS AGO, WE WERE ENGAGED. NOW I'M YOUR FIRST OFFICER.

YOUR *POINT*, COMMANDER SHELBY?

MY POINT IS, DON'T BE TOO HARD ON YOURSELF. BECAUSE I CAN SAY WITH CONFIDENCE THAT NOT EVEN *YOU* CAN BE IN TWO PLACES AT THE SAME TIME.

THAT WAS N THIS IS

ENEV IS A COLONY WORLD, ABOUT TWENTY HOURS OUT OF OUR ROUTE TO HARESH.

AND HOW LONG UNTIL THE MAGNETIC STORM GETS THERE?

TWENTY NINE HOURS, EIGHTEEN MINUTES, THIRTY ONE SECONDS.

WILL THAT LEAVE US ENOUGH TIME TO GET EVERYONE OFF THE PLANET?

I'VE WORKED IT OUT WITH BURGY. SHIFTING MANPOWER TO MAKE SURE ALL THE TRANSPORTER ROOMS ARE FULLY STAFFED AND RUNNING HOT, WE SHOULD *JUST* BE ABLE TO MAKE IT.

THE QUESTION BECOMES, WHAT ABOUT HARESH? HELPING *THIS* WORLD WILL DELAY OUR ARRIVAL THERE.

BUT FROM WHAT I UNDERSTAND, NOT HELPING THIS WORLD WILL GUARANTEE ITS DESTRUCTION. AM I RIGHT, LIEUTENANT?

EXACTLY RIGHT, CAPTAIN. THIS IS A PARTICULARLY VICIOUS MAGNETIC STORM...SOMETHING OF AN ANOMALY, REALLY.

I ESTIMATE AT LEAST AN EIGHTY PERCENT CASUALTY RATE... PERHAPS *HIGHER*.

YOU SAID IT'S A COLONY WORLD. SO WHY DOESN'T THE MOTHER WORLD DO SOMETHING ABOUT IT...

IT'S A COLONY THE SAME AS YOUR *AUSTRALIA* WAS A COLON FILLED WITH THE DREGS, TH MISFITS, THE UNWANTED O THE MOTHER WORLD... *INITIALLY*, AT LEAST. THA WAS SEVERAL GENERATION AGO...BUT THE STIGMA *REMAINS*.

IF THE ENEVIANS WERE WIPED OUT ENTIRELY THE MOTHER WORLD CALLED *ALORA*, I BELIEVE--WOULDN' CARE IN THE *LEAST*.

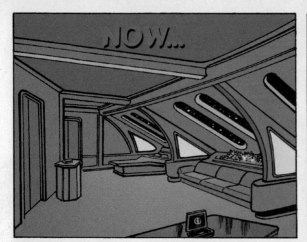

NOW...

DAMMIT.

DAMMIT!!

DAMN THE MAN.

COMPUTER.

WORKING.

FIRST OFFICER'S PERSONAL LOG, SUPPLEMENTAL...

THE EVACUATION MANUEVER ON ENEV COULD NOT HAVE GONE MORE SMOOTHLY.

"WITH VERY LITTLE TIME TO SPARE AND NO MARGIN FOR ERROR, THE EXCALIBUR MANAGED TO REMOVE THE ENTIRE POPULATION OF SEVERAL THOUSAND FROM THE COLONY WORLD OF ENEV BEFORE THE MAGNETIC STORM DEVASTATED IT."

"GRANTED, THE NUMBER OF PEOPLE BROUGHT ABOARD FAR EXCEEDED THE RECOMMENDED PASSENGER AND CREW COMPLEMENT, BUT IT WAS NOT FOR AN INDEFINITE PERIOD, AND OVERALL ADJUSTMENTS WERE MINIMAL...

"...WITH A FEW ISOLATED EXCEPTIONS."

"ONCE THE STORM HAD PASSED, NATURALLY WE RESTORED THEM AS QUICKLY AS WE COULD TO THEIR HOMEWORLD. THEIR LEADER TOLD CAPTAIN CALHOUN...

WE WILL NEVER FORGET YOU, CAPTAIN. WE OWE YOU AND YOUR CREW A DEBT WE CAN ONLY HOPE TO REPAY... AND LIKELY NEVER WILL.

"IT WAS VERY HEARTENING.

"OUR JOB DONE THERE, WE MOVED ON AS QUICKLY AS WE COULD TO HARESH...

"ONLY TO DISCOVER THAT OUR SAVING THE RESIDENTS OF THE COLONY WORLD HAD HAD FAR MORE CALAMITOUS CONSEQUENCES FOR HARESH THAN WE COULD HAVE IMAGINED.

"THE REDEEMERS HAD ARRIVED... CERTAIN FACTIONS HAD RESISTED... AND THE ENTIRE MATTER BECAME MOOT WHEN ONE OR MORE OF THE HARESH APPARENTLY ASSAULTED A REDEEMER HIGH PRIEST.

"THERE ARE SOME WHO BELIEVE THAT THE LETHAL DISEASE WHICH SOME REDEEMERS CARRY IN THEM IS EXAGGERATED. HOW CAN ONE VIRUS, WHEN UNLEASHED FROM A BLOODSTREAM, LAY WASTE TO AN ENTIRE WORLD?

"IT'S NO EXAGGERATION. THE VIRUS APPARENTLY MUTATES ALMOST INSTANTLY WHEN RELEASED, AND DOES NOT DISTINGUISH BETWEEN RACES, GENDERS OR AGES. YOUNG AND OLD DIED INSIDE OF A DAY. WITHIN THIRTY SIX HOURS... EVERYONE WAS GONE.

"MAC WAS DEVASTATED, FURIOUS...A DOZEN EMOTIONS, ONE SLAMMING UP AGAINST THE OTHER. BUT THEN, AFTER HE'D HAD TIME TO TAKE IT ALL IN, HE BECAME SOMETHING ELSE:

"DETERMINED

"I KNOW HIM, ALL TOO WELL. I KNOW HOW HE GETS. I KNOW HOW THAT SENSE OF RESPONSIBILITY KICKS IN. IT'S ONE OF THE THINGS I LOV--

"STRIKE LAST SENTENCE.

"IT'S ONE OF THE THINGS I *RESPECT* ABOUT HIM. BUT SOMETIMES...

"SOMETIMES IT CAN OVERWHELM HIS BETTER JUDGMENT.

"IT'S NOT SURPRISING, I SUPPOSE... CONSIDERING THE CIRCUMSTANCES THAT FORGED HIM.

AFTER ALL, HOW MANY
EIGHTEEN YEAR OLDS ARE
THERE WHO FEEL SUCH
RAGE THAT HIS PEOPLE ARE
A CONQUERED RACE...
THAT HE LEADS A PLANET-
WIDE REBELLION. A TEEN
WARLORD WHO REMADE THE
FACE OF A WORLD THROUGH
SHEER WILL POWER...

THOUGH ONE BATTLE, LATE IN
THE REBELLION, RESULTED IN A
REMAKING OF HIS OWN FACE.

"AFTER HIS PEOPLE WERE FREED, HE WOULD LIKELY HAVE
LIVED THE REMAINDER OF HIS LIFE THERE ON XENEX...
EXCEPT A CHANCE MEETING WITH JEAN-LUC PICARD
SENT HIS LIFE ON A DIFFERENT AND RATHER UNEXPECTED
COURSE. STILL...NO MATTER HOW FAR HE'S COME IN
THAT COURSE...

"HE'S ALWAYS BROUGHT SOME OF HIS ROOTS WITH HIM. AND HE'S NEVER GIVEN UP THE NOTION THAT HE CAN REMAKE THE WORLD IN AN IMAGE HE LIKES BETTER."

I SAW THE WAY HE LOOKED AROUND HARESH, LOOKED AT THOSE WHO DIED...

AND I KNOW, IN MY BONES, HE'S UP TO SOMETHING. SOMETHING THAT HE'D WANT TO KEEP FROM ME... ALTHOUGH WHETHER IT'S TO AVOID ARGUING WITH ME ABOUT IT, OR TO PROTECT ME IN THE EVENT OF STARFLEET INQUIRY, I CAN'T EVEN GUESS. PERHAPS A LITTLE OF BOTH.

WE STAYED IN ORBIT AROUND HARESH, STATING THAT HE WANTED EVERY SQUARE INCH OF THE PLANET SEARCHED FOR ANY POSSIBLE SURVIVORS. NOT LIKELY, BUT NOT UNREASONABLE. BUT THEN...

...HE STARTED HAVING "PRIVATE CONFERENCES..."

"...WITH DIFFERENT OFFICERS... ABOUT ODD TOPICS. HE CHATTED WITH *SOLETA* ABOUT SPEED, TRAJECTORY AND GRAVITY..."

"*MARK MCHENRY* ABOUT NAVIGATION..."

"CHIEF ENGINEER *BURGOYNE* ABOUT ENGINEERING CONFIGURATIONS..."

I DIDN'T WANT TO ASK MY OFFICERS TOO MUCH DETAIL ABOUT WHAT MAC WANTED TO KNOW. IT WOULD HAVE SEEMED AS IF I WAS...I DON'T KNOW...SPYING ON HIM. AS IF I DIDN'T TRUST HIM.

I BELIEVE IN THE CHAIN OF COMMAND. I'LL BE DAMNED IF I DO ANYTHING TO UNDERCUT IT.

I DON'T KNOW. MAYBE I'M BEING TOO PARANOID. MAC...

≶YAAAAWN≷

...CAN BRING THAT... OUT IN A PERSON. MAYBE IT'S... NOTHING.

I'VE BEEN OFF DUTY FOR hours... going over this in my mind...

Damn the man, he's making me crazy. End log.

LOG ENTRY ENDED.

CAPTAIN! YOU'RE UP RATHER LATE... OR EARLY, DEPENDING HOW YOU LOOK AT IT. WE DON'T GENERALLY SEE YOU ON NIGHTSIDE.

YOU'RE NOT DUE TO COME ON DUTY FOR ANOTHER HOUR.

COULDN'T SLEEP, MUELLER. SO I THOUGHT I'D TAKE US OUT ON A LITTLE... RIDE.

"LITTLE RIDE," SIR?

THAT'S RIGHT, X-O. UNLESS YOU HAD OTHER PLANS.

IF I MAY SAY SO... THIS IS A BIT *IRREGULAR*, CAPTAIN.

THE CAPTAIN OF A VESSEL SETTING COURSE AND SPEED? WHAT COULD BE MORE REGULAR THAN THAT, X-O?

DOING IT WHEN I'M *NOT HERE*...THE WAY YOU *NORMALLY* DO. INSTEAD OF DOING IT WHEN *COMMANDER SHELBY* ISN'T HERE...THE WAY YOU NORMALLY *DON'T*.

THANK YOU FOR THE INPUT, KAT.

I BUT LIVE TO SERVE, SIR.

MR. GOLD... HEADING 318 MARK 2. START US AT *WARP TWO*, WITH EXPONENTIAL ESCALATION AT POINT FIVE INCREMENTS OVER THE NEXT FORTY SEVEN SECONDS.

ON OUR WAY.

THAT'S.. AN AWFULLY SPECIFIC HEADING CAPTAIN. MAY I ASK IF THERE'S ANY PARTICULAR REASON?

JUST TESTING OUT A LITTLE THEORY, MR. TAKAHASHI.

AND THAT THEORY WOULD BE, SIR...?

THE THEORY, HASH, IS THAT, IF I GIVE A SERIES OF PECULIAR ORDERS, SOMEONE ON MY BRIDGE CREW WHO IS BUCKING TO BE *BUSTED* IN RANK WILL ASK ASSORTED QUESTIONS THAT HE NEED *NOT* BE ASKING.

INTERESTING THEORY.

CARE TO *TEST* IT?

NO, SIR.

YOU ARE WISE *BEYOND* YOUR YEARS, HASH.

BUT... CHANGING TIMELINES... STRICTLY *AGAINST REGS!* HE...HE *CAN'T...!*

HANG ON!!

WHAT IN THE--?

BARTENDER? ANOTHER ONE, WHEN YOU GET A CHANCE?

I STILL CAN'T BELIEVE WE'VE GONE BACK IN TIME, MOTHER!

TRUST ME, ROBIN. WHEN REALITY TURNS INSIDE OUT AND THE CHRONOMETERS ROLL BACK FOUR DAYS, EITHER WE'VE TIME TRAVELED OR ELSE SOMEONE'S BEEN SLIPPING SOME *EXTREMELY* INAPPROPRIATE SUBSTANCES INTO THE FOOD REPLICATORS.

BUT HAVE WE NOW *DISAPPEARED* FROM AROUND ENEV? ARE THEY NOW GOING TO DIE?

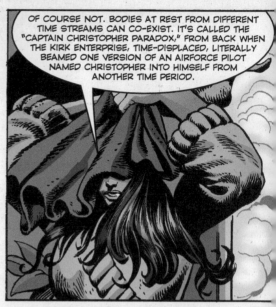

OF COURSE NOT. BODIES AT REST FROM DIFFERENT TIME STREAMS CAN CO-EXIST. IT'S CALLED THE "CAPTAIN CHRISTOPHER PARADOX," FROM BACK WHEN THE KIRK ENTERPRISE, TIME-DISPLACED, LITERALLY BEAMED ONE VERSION OF AN AIRFORCE PILOT NAMED CHRISTOPHER INTO HIMSELF FROM ANOTHER TIME PERIOD.

BUT WHAT HAPPENS TO THE EXCALIBUR FROM ENEV?

IT PROCEEDS IN ACCORDANCE WITH WHAT'S ALREADY HAPPENED...OR WHAT'S ALREADY *GOING* TO HAPPEN. THE THING IS, WHEN WE RETURN TO OUR OWN TIME, WE MUST DO SO SIGNIFICANTLY AFTER OUR FUTURE ARRIVAL AT HARESH. IF WE RUN INTO OURSELVES...

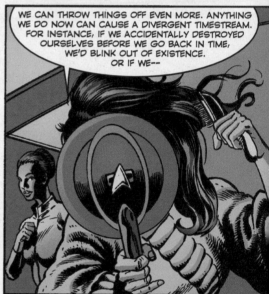

WE CAN THROW THINGS OFF EVEN MORE. ANYTHING WE DO NOW CAN CAUSE A DIVERGENT TIMESTREAM. FOR INSTANCE, IF WE ACCIDENTALLY DESTROYED OURSELVES BEFORE WE GO BACK IN TIME, WE'D BLINK OUT OF EXISTENCE. OR IF WE--

THANKS, MOTHER. I'M NOW MORE CONFUSED THAN EVER.

GLAD I COULD BE OF *HELP*, DEAR.

MEANING *WHAT?*

MEANING THAT IT APPEARS TO HAVE SOME SORT OF TIME DRIVE. FOLDS BACK TIME UPON ITSELF AND SLIPS THROUGH THE FOLD.

IS THAT *POSSIBLE?*

BY TODAY'S STANDARD? *NO.* ON THE OTHER HAND, ONLY A FEW CENTURIES AGO, WARP DRIVE WAS IMPOSSIBLE.

THE SHIP'S HAILING US, COMMANDER.

PUT THEM ON SCREEN, LEFLER.

ON SCREEN, AYE.

STARSHIP *EXCALIBUR.* THIS IS THE TIMESHIP *RELATIVITY.* CAPTAIN BRAXTON COMMANDING.

"TIMESHIP?" DID YOU SAY--

TIMESHIP, YES. WE NEED TO SPEAK ON A MATTER OF SOME URGENCY AND EXTREME *DELICACY,* COMMANDER. WE CAN EITHER BEAM OVER THERE, OR BRING YOU HERE. WE'LL GIVE YOU A MOMENT TO DECIDE. BRAXTON OUT.

I SURE AS HELL *WOULDN'T* GO OVER THERE.

WHO *ARE* THESE GUYS?

TRUSTING THEM IMPLICITLY IS ILLOG--

EXCUSE ME... I DON'T RECALL SOLICITING OPINIONS. ROBIN...CAN YOU GET A READING ON THEIR ARMAMENT?

MY GOD.

SPECIFICS, LEFLER, NOT STARTLED EXCLAMATIONS, IF YOU PLEASE.

EIGHT MAIN BATTERIES CONSISTING OF PURE ANTI-PROTON CANNONS. SIX PHASER BATTERIES WITH CHARGE CAPACITY OF 1.5 KILLMEGS EACH. FOUR-PLY ENERGY SHIELDS OF--

MY GOD.

THAT'S NOT ALL. HER HULL CONTAINS METAL ALLOYS I'VE *NEVER* SEEN... PLUS AT LEAST ONE ELEMENT NOT ON THE PERIODIC TABLE.

IF THEY PURPORT TO BE SOME SORT OF "TIMESHIP" FROM THE FUTURE... IT IS, COMMANDER, AS GOOD AN EXPLANATION AS *ANY,* AND BETTER THAN ANY OTHERS *I* CAN SUGGEST.

IF THEIR CAPTAIN IS REQUESTING AN *AUDIENCE* RATHER THAN JUST BLOWING US OUT OF SPACE...

I RECOMMEND YOU TAKE HIM *UP* ON IT.

I APPRECIATE THE TIME, COMMANDER.

THEN AGAIN, TIME IS YOUR STOCK IN TRADE, ISN'T IT.

SO THIS IS CALHOUN'S READY ROOM. JUST AS THE TEXTS *DESCRIBED*.

I'M SO *PLEASED* WE'RE ON THE HISTORICAL PLACES OF INTEREST TOUR, CAPTAIN. NOW IF YOU WOULDN'T MIND--

GETTING TO THE POINT? ABSOLUTELY. ALTHOUGH, FOR TEMPORAL SECURITY REASONS, I'LL KEEP THINGS TO A MINIMUM.

WE REPRESENT A FUTURE AGENCY, CHARGED WITH MAINTAINING THE TIME LINE AND *DISCOURAGING* ANY CHRONOLOGICAL MEDDLING. IN SHORT...THE SORT OF ACTIVITY IN WHICH YOUR CAPTAIN IS PRESENTLY *ENGAGED*.

THIS WORLD'S FATE-- COLD AS IT MAY SOUND-- WAS TO BE WIPED OUT. CALHOUN IS TAKING A TREMENDOUS CHANCE BY ATTEMPTING TO THWART THAT FATE.

WHAT WOULD YOU SUGGEST I DO?

RELIEVE CALHOUN OF *COMMAND*. WHATEVER EXCUSES HE MAY HAVE MADE, WE *BOTH* KNOW HE IS IN CLEAR VIOLATION OF STARFLEET DIRECTIVES. YOU HAVE AN *OBLIGATION* TO DO SO--NOT JUST TO YOURSELF AND TO THE FLEET, BUT TO ALL OF *TIME*.

SO LET'S SEE IF I'VE GOT THIS: AN "OFFICER" I DON'T KNOW, ON A SHIP WHOSE AUTHORITY I DON'T RECOGNIZE, IS ASKING ME TO CHALLENGE MY CAPTAIN.

I'M ASKING YOU TO DO, PRECISELY NO *MORE* AND NO LESS THAN, WHAT YOU KNOW TO BE RIGHT.

"CAPTAIN'S LOG, SUPPLEMENTAL. THE NEGOTIATIONS ON HARESH BETWEEN MINISTER RIZPAK AND HIS MAIN POLITICAL RIVAL, SUBMINISTER FERMIT, HAVE NOT GONE AS SMOOTHLY AS I'D HOPED.

"I'VE BEGUN TO SUSPECT THAT MUCH OF THE OPPOSITION MOVEMENT IS MOTIVATED, NOT SIMPLY FROM A CURIOUSITY ABOUT WHAT THE REDEEMERS MAY HAVE TO 'OFFER,' BUT ALSO POLITICAL *MANEUVERING* DESIGNED TO PUT FERMIT INTO A BETTER POSITION OF POWER FOR THE NEXT *ELECTION*.

"I HAVE TRIED EMPHASIZING TO THEM THAT THE ELECTION WILL NEVER BE HELD IF MATTERS KEEP ON THIS COURSE, ALTHOUGH I HAVE NOT MENTIONED THE TOTAL DEVASTATION I'VE 'FORESEEN.'

"HOWEVER, FERMIT AND HIS FOLLOWERS REMAIN *ADAMANT*, AND TIME IS RUNNING OUT. SO I HAVE BEEN ENDEAVORING TO FIND SOME SORT OF...ELEGANT MEANS... OF SETTLING THE ENTIRE DISPUTE.

"AS LUCK WOULD HAVE IT... THE HARESH SOCIETY TURNS OUT TO BE ONE WITH A PROUD TRADITION OF *DUELING*. I MAY BE ABLE TO USE THAT TO SOME... SLIGHT ADVANTAGE.

MINISTER, I HAVE TO *PROTEST* AGAIN! FERMIT TOOK OFFENSE AT *MY* COMMENTS! I'M THE ONE WHO CALLED HIM BLIND AND A FOOL. IT SHOULD BE ME FIGHTING HIM! AS LEADER, IT'S *MY* RESPONSIBILITY!

BUT AS A LEADER...AND A *GUEST*...YOUR STATUS HERE PRECLUDES SUCH A DIRECT CONFLICT. IT WOULD BE... IMPOLITE.

THEN I COULD DELEGATE... TO *KEBRON* HERE!

AND MISS SEEING CWAN GETTING *DECAPITATED?*

YOU'RE NOT *HELPING,* LIEUTENANT.

SORRY.

GO, SI CWAN.

RAH.

KLAAANG

BESIDES, AS THE OFFENDED PARTY, FERMIT HAD THE RIGHT TO CHOOSE *WHICH* OF YOUR PARTY WOULD REPRESENT YOU.

YOU FORGET, AMBASSADOR CWAN IS NOT ONLY A *THALLONIAN,* BUT PART OF THE ERSTWHILE ROYAL FAMILY. MANY OF MY PEOPLE HAVE LITTLE LOVE FOR THE TIME WHEN CWAN AND HIS KIND HELD SWAY OVER US.

FERMIT NO DOUBT CONSIDERS THIS AN OPPORTUNITY FOR PAYBACK... AND TO LOOK GOOD TO HIS FOLLOWERS.

N-NO...

NO!!

NO!!

NO!!

WHATEVER.

WUMM

OH, THANK THE GODS. IF HE'D KILLED HER MATE, MY SISTER WOULD *NEVER* HAVE FORGIVEN ME...

THIS JUST GETS BETTER AND BETTER.

FERMIT... IS YOUR *BROTHER-IN-LAW?*

"DO WHAT'S RIGHT."

THAT ALSO SOUNDS LIKE HIM.

WHAT YOU *FEEL* IS RIGHT, OR WHAT YOU *KNOW* IS RIGHT?

IT'S NOT THAT *SIMPLE*, KAT. IT'S A MATTER OF--

WHOA!!!

SORRY.

SORRY! YOU ALMOST CUT MY *NOSE* OFF!!

WOULDN'T WANT TO DO *THAT*. ESPECIALLY IF IT'S FOR THE PURPOSE OF SPITING YOUR FACE.

IS THAT SUPPOSED TO *MEAN* SOMETHING?

IT CAN MEAN WHATEVER YOU *WANT* IT TO MEAN.

THAT'S THE BEST I'M GOING TO GET OUT OF YOU FOR ADVICE, ISN'T IT?

PRETTY MUCH. AREN'T YOU GLAD YOU CAME TO ME FOR IT?

ACTUALLY, IN A WEIRD WAY... I *AM*.

WHY DID YOU TAKE UP *FENCING*, ANYWAY?

TO RELIEVE SEXUAL TENSION.

YOU SHOULD *TRY* IT.

TOUCHÉ.

CAPTAIN BRAXTON...LONG RANGE SENSORS INDICATE THE REDEEMER VESSEL IS EN ROUTE.

WELL, IF WE'RE PICKING THEM UP, THEN THAT MEANS THE EXCALIBUR WILL HAVE THEM IN THEIR SIGHTS FAIRLY SOON AS WELL.

TACTICAL ASSESSMENT, MR. DUCANE: CAN THE HARESH SURFACE-TO-SPACE GROUND DEFENSES OVERPOWER THE REDEEMER SHIP?

ON THEIR OWN? VERY UNLIKELY. THE EXCALIBUR WILL BE WHAT TIPS THE BALANCE.

VERY WELL. THEN LET'S TIP HER BACK.

MR. DUCANE, RAISE THE EXCALIBUR FOR ME, IF YOU PLEASE.

CAPTAIN... HAIL FROM THE RELATIVITY.

ON SCREEN. LET'S SEE WHERE WE STAND.

CAPTAIN CALHOUN. INTERESTING. I WAS EXPECTING SOMEONE TALLER.

IN BATTLE, I'M POSITIVELY STATUESQUE. LET'S HOPE YOU WON'T HAVE TO SEE ME THAT WAY.

INDEED... SINCE I'D HATE TO BE THE ONE TO CUT YOU DOWN TO SIZE.

GOD, MAC...HOW AM I SUPPOSED TO BUILD A FUTURE WITH YOU WHEN YOU SAY THINGS LIKE THAT?

WHEN I'M WITH YOU, IT FEELS SO RIGHT... BUT THEN SOMETHING MAKES IT GO WRONG.

TO HELL WITH BED! DIDN'T YOU *HEAR* ME? WHAT ABOUT OUR *FUTURE*?! ABOUT BUILDING TOMORROW!

COME BACK TO BED, EPPY.

FUNNY THING, EPPY-- HOUSES, PALACES, STARSHIP... THEY DON'T EXIST UNLESS WE BUILD THEM. BUT TOMORROW? IT SHOWS UP WHETHER WE BUILD IT OR NOT.

ALL WE CAN DO IS BUILD THE BEST TODAY POSSIBLE-- AND HOPE THAT TOMORROW COPIES IT, AS IT SEES FIT.

LET'S DO WHAT'S RIGHT FOR TODAY...

...AND LET THE FUTURE SORT ITSELF OUT.

WELL, COMMANDER? DO YOU HAVE SOMETHING TO SAY TO ME?

YES. LET'S...

...LET'S DO WHAT'S RIGHT FOR TODAY, CAPTAIN...AND LET THE FUTURE SORT ITSELF OUT...

DAMN. WISH *I'D* SAID THAT.

AND I WISH YOU'D SAID SOMETHING ELSE. BRAXTON OUT.

MR. DUCANE...

AYE, CAPTAIN...?

OPEN FIRE ON THE *EXCALIBUR*. WEAPONS AT QUARTER STRENGTH.

WE JUST WANT TO *HOBBLE* THE HORSE... NOT BREAK A LEG.

CAPTAIN! THEIR WEAPONS ARE LOCKING ON.

SHIELDS UP. GO TO RED ALERT, ALL HANDS TO BATTLE STATIONS.

OOOOF!!

UNHHH!!!

MAIN PHASER BARRAGE... NO MEASURABLE EFFECT. OUR OWN SHIELDS ARE AT SIXTY PERCENT AND FALLING.

WHAT DO YOU CALL THOSE *HEAVY GUNS* OF THEIRS?

LOUD.

ANTI-PROTON CANNONS...BY MY CALCULATIONS, AT LESS THAN A THIRD OF FULL STRENGTH.

YOU'RE SAYING THEY'RE FIRING *WARNING* SHOTS?

ESSENTIALLY, YES.

ENGINEERING TO BRIDGE...

BRIDGE HERE.

ENSIGN BETH INFORMS ME THAT ANOTHER THREE HITS LIKE THAT, AND WE LOSE OUR SHIELDS.

CAN YOU SHORE UP DEFENSES BY CONCENTRATING ALL POWER ON *FORWARD DEFLECTORS?*

AYE, SIR, BUT...

DO IT. MCHENRY...SET A COLLISION COURSE. FULL IMPULSE POWER.

DID YOU SAY...?

YOU HEARD ME.

COLLISION COURSE! ARE YOU SURE?

POSITIVE, SIR, HE'S COMING RIGHT FOR US.

CAPTAIN! ARE YOU INSANE? VEER OFF IMMEDIATELY, BEFORE--

BEFORE WHAT, CAPTAIN? BEFORE WE DIE?

I WAS SORT OF HOPING YOU'D SAY THAT. BECAUSE IF YOU'RE FROM THE FUTURE...WHY, THEN YOU'D KNOW IF THIS IS OUR TIME TO GO. SINCE YOU'RE TRYING TO PREVENT OUR DEMISE, I'M GOING TO GUESS THAT IT'S NOT. IN WHICH CASE, I'D SUGGEST YOU GET THE HELL OUT OF OUR WAY. OTHERWISE YOU'LL BE CHANGING THE PAST, AND WE WOULDN'T WANT THAT.

I CAN STILL CRIPPLE YOUR SHIP WITHOUT DESTROYING HER--

NO YOU CAN'T. BECAUSE IF YOU CRIPPLE HER, I'LL TRIGGER THE SELF-DESTRUCT FAILSAFE PROTOCOL AND BLOW US TO BITS. SO OUR ADVENTURES WILL STILL END RIGHT HERE IN A MILLION PIECES.

YOU WOULDN'T KILL YOURSELF AND YOUR CREW--! THAT'S--!

YOU'RE THE ONE WHO INQUIRED AS TO WHETHER I WAS INSANE, BRAXTON.

NEVER ASK A QUESTION THAT YOU DON'T REALLY WANT THE ANSWER TO.

GET OUT...

...OF OUR WAY.

WELL, THIS COULD BE INTERESTING.

HARESH DEFENSE SYSTEMS HAVING *NO* MEASURABLE IMPACT ON REDEEMER VESSEL, CAPTAIN. THEY'RE PREPARING TO RETURN FIRE ON THE SURFACE OF HARESH.

LET'S SEE WHAT *WE* CAN DO TO HELP.

BRING ALL PHASER BATTERIES TO BEAR ON--

SIR! THE RELATIVITY JUST PUT HERSELF BETWEEN THE *REDEEMERS* AND US!

INCOMING!

ALL HANDS, BRACE FOR IMPACT!

SHWAAAM

STAY FOCUSED! WATCH THE *LEVELS!!!*

KEEP IT *TOGETHER,* PEOPLE!!

OOOOOF!!!

ALLOW THE ENEVIANS TO DIE... BECAUSE OF WHAT THEY *MIGHT* BECOME, CENTURIES HENCE? COME STRAIGHT HERE AND SAVED THE HARESH? EXCEPT... WITHOUT THE ENEVIANS AROUND, PERHAPS THE HARESH WOULD HAVE BECOME HEARTLESS CONQUERORS...

MAC, IF YOU START SECOND-GUESSING EVERY STEP YOU MAKE, YOU'LL--

GO INSANE? WELL, THAT WOULD ANSWER BRAXTON'S QUESTION, AT LEAST.

DO YOU SEE AT LEAST, THOUGH, WHY I KEEP HARPING ABOUT RULES SOMETIMES BEING *GOOD* THINGS, EVEN THOUGH THEY *ARE* RULES? WHY YOUR NOTION OF CREATING A UNIVERSE OF "RIGHT" OVER "WRONG" ISN'T AS *EASY* AS ALL THAT...BECAUSE YOU CAN NEVER FORESEE EVERY OUTCOME?

THAT TIME TRAVEL IS-- AT BEST--

A DOUBLE-EDGED SWORD?

EXACTLY.

I'M *STARTING* TO...FOR WHAT THAT'S *WORTH*.

IT'S *WORTH* QUITE A BIT, ACTUALLY.

ALTHOUGH I *AM* PLEASED THAT YOU OPTED TO SLINGSHOT US BACK INTO OUR FUTURE RATHER THAN JUST SIT AROUD AND ALLOW TIME TO PASS. THE LONGER WE WERE IN THE PAST, THE MORE CHANCE WE HAD OF DISRUPTING... EVEN INADVERTENTLY... THE FUTURE.

ONE... SLIGHT PROBLEM, THOUGH. THE BACK-AND-FORTH PLAYED HAVOC WITH OUR CHRONOMETERS. WE JUST FINISHED RECALIBRATING AFTER RETURNING TO OUR TIME AND, WELL...

WELL *WHAT*?

WE OVERSHOT. SLIGHTLY. BY, UHM...

SIXTEEN MONTHS.

WONDERFUL. WELL, WE'RE *NOT* GOING TO TRY AND HEAD *BACK* AGAIN. I'VE *HAD* IT WITH TIME TRAVEL.

UNDERSTOOD, BUT... STARFLEET THOUGHT WE'D BEEN *DESTROYED*. NOW THEY WANT TO KNOW WHERE THE HELL WE'VE *BEEN* FOR NEARLY A YEAR AND A HALF.

TELL THEM...

TELL THEM WE'VE BEEN WORKING--

WORKING, SIR?

THAT'S RIGHT, EPPY. TO BE SPECIFIC...

TELL THEM WE'VE BEEN PUTTING IN A *LOT* OF OVERTIME.

MIC DAR '00

STAR TREK ®

What you've just read – unless you're one of those folks, like me, who comes bac
here to read this part first – are some of the great Star Trek comic book stories
published by WildStorm Productions/DC Comics in the first year of our publishin
agreement with Paramount Pictures.

If you are a regular comic book reader, then you might have encountered some of
these stories in their first incarnations on the racks at your local comic book shop.
But if you found this in a bookstore, chances are you don't even know you have a
local comic shop. Most likely, you do. Look it up. You might find you like it
there. Certainly, you can find new Star Trek comics there, every single month.

This particular collection is written by a handful of novelists, all of whom have also
written comics. Tony Isabella and Bob Ingersoll are best known for comics work
and for long-running columns in a magazine called "Comics Buyer's Guide," but
they've written a novel about everyone's favorite patriot, Captain America, called
"Liberty's Torch." K. W. Jeter has written groundbreaking science fiction, includi
"Dr. Adder," "Bladerunner 2: The Edge of Human," and "Noir." Peter David is
possibly the most popular STAR TREK novelist of all time, author of the extrem
popular line of New Frontier stories, and a busy comics writer to boot.

Not to short the artists – Aaron Lopresti with Randy Emberlin, Toby Cypress wit
Jason Martin and Mark Irwin, and Michael Collins with David Roach have all turn
in exceptional work; each style different, but each one uniquely suited to the story
being told. Which, after all, is what comics are all about.

So once again, we invite you...if you're not a regular comics fan, then give these
stories a read. There's some great visual storytelling going on in comics these da
If you missed these the first time out, who knows what great stuff you're missing
out on now?

– Jeff Mariotte
Senior Editor

Write to us at:
STAR TREK c/o WildStorm Productions
7910 Ivanhoe Ave. #438
La Jolla, CA 92037
or e-mail us at paramountcomics@wildstorm.com

Nog

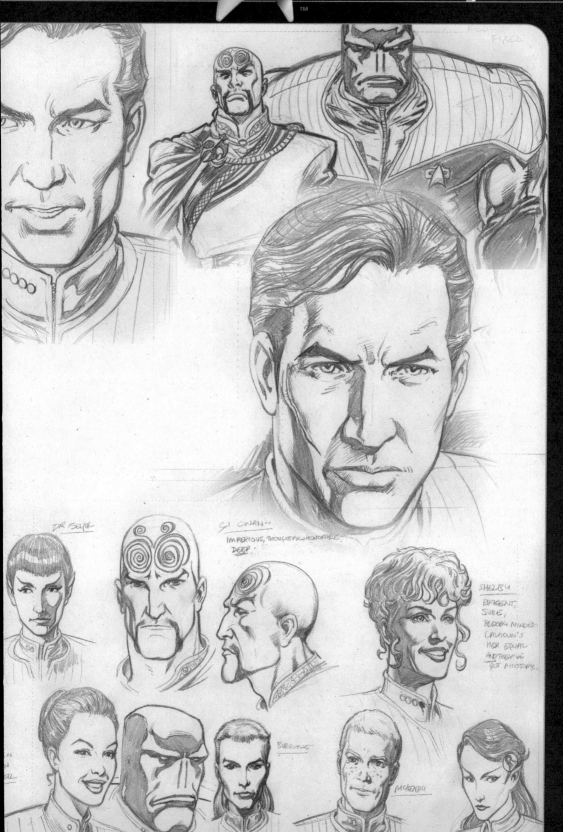

DR SELAR

SI CWAN..
IMPERIOUS, THOUGHTFUL, HONORABLE
DEEP

SHELBY
EFFICIENT,
SURE,
BLOODY-MINDED.
CALHOUN'S
HER EQUAL
AND THEY'VE
GOT A HISTORY...

BURGOYNE

MCKENZIE